For Guy 2

UNION JACK

All the best

Christopher Hitchens

About the author

Charles Mitford Cust comes from a branch of the same Mitford family tree as bore the famous literary sisters Nancy and Jessica. Appropriately for the subject of this book, his ancestry has fielded four generals, a lord chief justice and two Speakers of the House of Commons. An accomplished entrepreneur turned writer, he has survived many hair-raising international adventures including escaping hostage takers in the Middle East after being held captive for three months. It would be fair to say that he has seen and done it all. Union Jack draws on both his broad business experience and these larger-than-life-Bond-style escapades.

UNION JACK

Charles Mitford Cust

This book is available as a paperback
or in Kindle format from Amazon

First published in 2015 by
Charterhouse Books Ltd

British Library Cataloguing in Publication Data
A catalogue record of this book is available from the
British Library

ISBN 978-0-9513293-9-9

Typeset by Exe Valley Design & Print Ltd, Exeter

Contents

Foreword

by Sir Henry Chetwyn-Fraser
private secretary to Jack Nelson

Jack Nelson is the most unusual man I have ever known. Upon first meeting him I was immediately struck by the odd combination of his quiet, unassuming demeanour and the dangerous aura he projected. One realised straight away that he was born to be a man of destiny, to lead and to rule, and it somehow seemed appropriate that such an extraordinary man, like the most illustrious historical figure to bear the same name, Horatio himself, would come to the aid of Britain at her darkest hour and save her.

Jack had never been involved in politics. After Charterhouse and Cambridge, where he read engineering, he followed the family tradition by joining the Royal Marines, and just before his twenty-ninth birthday, he became one of the youngest Royal Marines to achieve the rank of major. He served in the SBS Special Forces, the maritime equivalent of the SAS, on several secret missions behind enemy lines in various conflict zones before retiring from active service due to wounds received in combat. He had been offered promotion to lieutenant colonel if he took up an administrative position in Intelligence and Strategic Planning, one regarded as a fast track to the top, but he responded by saying that deskwork bored him and he preferred to seek new challenges elsewhere.

I very much doubt at the time that his ambitions included running the country. From what I have gathered, he never showed any interest in politics other than to express a deep distrust of politicians themselves. Instead he started inventing products and manufacturing them in England, some of which were quite successful. He could have undoubtedly made far more money had he subcontracted the manufacture abroad but he refused to do this, sometimes to the chagrin of his investors.

There is one thing that defines Jack above all else: his near fanatical patriotism. He put his life on the line in combat for the country he loves, and when one heard him giving a briefing to his section chiefs in 10 Downing Street, one was left in no doubt that if it came to the crunch, he would always be prepared to do so. I never felt that he forced his patriotism on others in such meetings, but occasionally one would glimpse the passion which so clearly drove him, lying just beneath the surface. When this happened, it was hard not to feel moved oneself.

Jack's other notable characteristics include his classlessness and humour, which I suppose one could describe as the dry gallows humour typical of military men. But there were very few briefings at Number 10 during which he failed to make us all laugh. Equally, he has the ability to converse with people of all walks of life. I suppose, once again, this was due to his time in Special Forces, where often an officer must live for weeks or months in a small, tightly knit unit comprising men from every background. I imagine also that running his factory later on Civvy Street, will have exposed him to a broader range of people than he would perhaps have otherwise encountered.

A consequence of this unusual aspect of his make up is that although he comes from a somewhat privileged background, one senses he has a deep connection with the everyday working man, and that they in turn accept his totally unpatronising approach to interacting with them. People can always sense genuineness, and Jack is genuine to the core. When he talks to you, he gives you his full attention and he makes you feel like you are the only person whose opinion he cares about.

While I appreciate that you must be curious to know, I am sorry to say that I am unable to expand much on the exact details of how Jack pulled off his coup. I would do so if I knew but I honestly do not, nor I suspect, ever will anyone apart from his co-conspirators. All I know is that somehow he managed to persuade a sufficient number of senior figures in the military establishment that the country was in dire danger and that it had to be saved.

I think it is safe to assume that he will have promised the Armed Forces very substantial increases in their budgets in return for their cooperation, which will have been a strong incentive at a time when MPs, in an all-party vote, had just passed a motion to dramatically cut military spending, causing great unrest throughout the already overstretched armed services.

In Jack's view things had simply gone too far. The bizarre upside-down prioritisation of the PC culture was taking the country to the very brink of disaster. Britain had become a society in which the rights of criminals and terrorists were taking precedence over those of the normal, law-abiding population, a place where thanks to the PC brigade, or the PCB as Jack named them, millions of pounds of taxpayers' money would be spent defending the rights of an extremist hate preacher who advocated acts of violent terrorism against the population, rather than used to look after the desperately ill or the dismally poor.

To add insult to injury, in almost every case, not only would taxpayers' money be spent by the PCB to protect the terrorist in question from being deported, but also to continue to provide him and his family with an unnecessarily luxurious house, generous benefits and a car.

In Jack's view Britain had become a country where children were allowed to grow obese and were totally undisciplined because no one had dared to do anything to stop these undesirable situations developing, due to the endless laws and regulations imposed by the PCB. Indeed, Jack believed that the sinister influence of the PCB had created a heart-disease and diabetes time bomb just waiting to explode on an overstretched NHS of the future, and an entire generation of lawless thugs with no regard or respect for other people.

To this bubbling cauldron was added the news that Britain's Armed Forces budgets were to be slashed yet again to pay for more housing and healthcare for the limitless numbers of parasitic benefit-seeking immigrants pouring into Britain from the poorest countries in the EU. This at a time when the forces were under more pressure than at any time since World War II, fighting as they were in no fewer than three war zones in the Middle East.

It is a credit to the astonishing professionalism of the combined Special Forces teams involved and to Jack's leadership that there were no fatalities during the coup. The only people who were shot at during the night of the coup were armed protection officers of the Metropolitan Police. But despite the fact that they were firing live ammunition at Jack's men, they were all neutralised by highly accurate sniper fire using harmless tranquilising darts shot from special rifles. They were left with only a nasty hangover when they awoke several hours later. Apart from some superficial injuries sustained during hand-to-hand fighting or from falling over when tranquilised, none were seriously hurt.

Jacks men seized control of the entire political infrastructure during that eventful night. Every single MP was grabbed from his or her location and taken under armed escort in secure vans or military helicopters to a heavily defended military camp in Wiltshire. There they were guarded by a mechanised brigade including two infantry battalions, several squadrons of main battle tanks, heavy artillery, and three squadrons of fully armed Apache attack helicopters.

These forces had gathered on Salisbury Plain, which since World War II has been regarded as Britain's largest military playground, in the belief they were taking part in a large-scale exercise. The truth was only revealed to the soldiers and their officers on the following morning, when at the same time the blank ammunition was replaced by live rounds.

The massive show of firepower used to guard the captured MPs was mobilised mainly in case the UN decided to intervene, which it did not – further evidence that Jack had sympathetic friends in high places.

I have no proof, but personally I suspect NATO may have played its part here. The very real fear that one of its most important members was about to be severely reduced in capability by financial cutbacks may well have led to NATO leaders putting high-level pressure on the UN to stand aside.

With the entire British Armed Forces on side, once their commanding officers had explained to all ranks that a coup had occurred, and one that would work very much in their favour, the only possible armed opposition could have come from the Armed Response and Diplomatic Protection units of the police. However, when these units realised what they would be up against, they sensibly capitulated and surrendered their weapons without a shot being fired. There were no hard feelings expressed towards them for doing their duty on the night of the coup, and once disarmed, they were allowed to return home to their families to await orders.

In some cases the capture of individual members of parliament on the night of the coup caused some considerable personal embarrassment. This was because they were seized while engaged in the kind of activities they would have preferred their constituents not to hear about. Many were snatched from apartments belonging to their mistresses or to prostitutes, in which they were found engaged in elaborate sex games while displaying more sartorial imagination than one would normally associate with a respectable member of parliament.

Some of these kinky outfits were more elaborate than others. I recall that one cabinet minister was wearing a bright-blue baby's romper suit while lying in an oversized cot and being bottle-fed by a high-class prostitute, when he was snatched. Another leading political figure was picked up in a call-girl's apartment while dressed as a pet chihuahua and wearing a lead.

Some were taken from the likes of S&M brothels. More than one MP had to be unbound rather than bound by his captors. In one raid several senior political figures from both sides of the house were grabbed while participating in a Roman-style orgy in a Turkish bathhouse.

All in all, one might say, just the normal activities of your average MP on a Thursday night before returning to the respectable family home in the country on Friday. It was no coincidence, then, that Jack chose a Thursday night for the coup.

Naturally, in every case plenty of incriminating photographs were taken before the MPs were removed from their compromising situations, only in order to assist the smooth transition of power, you understand. All it took to get the various civil service departments to fully cooperate with Jack's new regime in the morning was the threat to release various very clear photographs taken during the raids to the tabloid press, which, it was promised, would be shortly followed by some very interesting high-definition videos on YouTube.

I never plucked up the courage to ask him. But I feel that one can assume it was a good bet that Jack had some help from MI5 and the other intelligence services concerning the exact whereabouts of every single MP in the country, and indeed of those abroad in places like Brussels, on that fateful Thursday night.

While the raids took place, the coup conspirators deployed ultra-high-tech warfare transmission-jamming equipment, set up in key locations throughout the country, to ensure there was an overnight TV and radio blackout. Also apart from 999 calls, all mobile phone networks and landlines were shut down because the central telecoms distribution hub at Milton Keynes was under the control of Jack's Special Forces. This action also enabled Jack's men to effect a temporary suspension of all broadband services throughout the country so that the population could not communicate with each other via social media.

On television at 9 a.m. on Friday morning, Jack addressed an extremely surprised population, almost none of whom realised that a coup had taken place the night before. He explained why he had taken such a drastic step and detailed the issues he intended to address. He spoke with such passion and sincerity that within half an hour the vast majority of the listeners were mesmerised by him.

He assured them that there were no sinister implications for the average person and asked them to carry on their lives as normal while he set about making Britain a better place to live for them. He emphasised that there were no restrictions on travel abroad or on their movements generally. He told them there was no question of the country being under martial law or anything of that nature, and as the police and other services were operating as normal, they had nothing to fear. They should all just go about their business and leisure activities as they please.

His honest schoolboyish, old-fashioned, patriotic approach appealed to the public. They cheered everywhere when he mentioned his intention to build a new Royal Yacht and to relaunch a new version of Concorde so the world would realise that Britain was back.

He finished his hour-long speech by stating that it was essential for Britain to be regarded as a democratic country, so he was going to give himself just five years to sort everything out before returning the MPs to power. In the meantime he would give them a taste of real life by sending them under armed guard to Canada to work in the wastelands in all weathers, repairing railway lines. This went down very well with the population, who gave him a spontaneous standing ovation all around the country when he finished, whether they had been watching their screens at home in their living rooms or kitchens or at the office or huddled several layers deep in silent awe in TV and electronics retailers.

So that morning Jack Nelson, a hitherto unknown Royal Marine, through his sheer sincerity, his common-sense reasoning, his in-touch-with-the-normal-person attitude and his breath-of-fresh-air, old-fashioned but somehow desperately appealing patriotism, and in no little part his sheer charisma, won the hearts and minds of the entire country in less than a single hour in a way no duplicitous, self-serving politician could ever hope to do in a hundred lifetimes.

That is the magic of the man, and now you can read a transcript of a recording he made with me before he left the country on the eve of the elections. He asked me to turn it into a book after he was gone, to explain the reasoning behind his every decision and action while in power.

It is far more than just the confessions of a dictator, entertaining though they may be in their own right thanks to Jack's unique brand of dry humour. Rather it is a wake-up call to us, showing just how much we have been manipulated by politicians of all parties and their sinister PC pressure groups. It is also a reminder that if we choose, we can be free again if we stop being afraid and refuse to allow these despicable, small-minded little people to interfere with our lives.

Jack Nelson not only saved this nation of ours, he also woke us from the apathetic slumber, in which politicians and the PC pressure groups rely on us to remain, and showed us how to live as free men. Then, in the typical selfless humility of so many of his brave comrades-in-arms fighting for our freedom around the world, having done his duty, he quietly slipped away, without even expecting so much as a thank you.

This is his unedited story in his own words.

Prologue

This is Jack Nelson speaking. Well I have to say it is hard to believe that nearly five years have passed since I took over the job of running Britain as I refer to it. I suppose it sounds a bit more acceptable to me than the alternative description of my role in our island's history. I don't like the term *dictator*; it smacks of political extremism, and one thing I certainly am not is political. Left, right or centre, they are all just as bad to me.

Nor for that matter am I a racist as most dictators are. I have served in the Armed Forces and fought in combat with people from the widest diversity of cultural heritages imaginable and have learnt to embrace their differences and to respect them all. I am not interested in the colour of a man's skin but I am interested in the colour of his character.

All I care about is our country and its people and that has nothing to do with politics in any form. For me it has all been about sorting out the country's problems in straightforward and practical ways and getting the job done.

I gave myself five years to get Britain back on track, and now that I have achieved this I have unfrozen the democratic process of conventional government and released the former MPs of all parties from exile in Canada, where for the first time for most of them, they were forced to actually work for a living.

I am sure they have found hauling timber and repairing railway tracks and suchlike an insightful experience and that they will return as more rounded and useful members of society, certainly more in touch with the general population, who for the most part, it would appear, have not missed their forced absence at all.

When they return, they will now find Britain is certainly very different from the country they left. Crime is non-existent; the prisons are empty apart from one infamous war criminal serving a full-life sentence in Belmarsh high-security prison. The national debt has been paid off, there is now full employment, the school children are slimmer and fitter, the NHS is well funded and highly efficient, the motorways are seldom ever congested, public transport is cheaper, pensions are higher, and university education is optionally free.

Not to mention that Britain has regained its pride. The Queen will soon have a brand-new larger and more luxurious Royal Yacht and has just taken delivery of the first new *Concorde II*, which although closely based on the original, is even more elegantly beautiful and faster. It was christened *Pride of Britain* and finished in royal blue, with the royal coat of arms embossed in real gold extracted from a Cornish mine on the tail fin.

Now once again, when our monarch arrives by yacht or plane, the world will be reminded that we are the most innovative and technically competent nation in the world, and, just as importantly, that we can never be equalled in terms of style and panache.

Funnily enough, on the subject of the new Royal Yacht, it was actually on the day they decommissioned *The Britannia* that I realised the writing was on the wall for Britain; not because of what it was but because I realised what it really represented. I mean what it *really* represented – it *was* Britain; it was you and me. It represented what made us the people we are in the eyes of the world – maybe not the great nation we once were, which in old days moved earth and heaven as Tennyson put it, but still a highly important player on the world stage.

The vessel was a floating embassy of British calm in the world's tumultuous ocean of insecure cultures. It was an elegant reminder to other countries that we are still the most sensible, equitable, civilised and dependable race on the planet.

Yes, it was on that sad day that I realised how dangerous the ego-centric jumped-up little squirts who sat in parliament had become to the future of this country. I mean, for God's sake, when they decommissioned *The Britannia*, they made the Queen weep and they robbed us of the last vestige of our national pride. How dare they do that, I thought. That was the day I swore I would put things right and I started plotting my coup.

When the politicians return from the Canadian wastelands, a lot slimmer and fitter, I might add, they are going to find it a great deal harder to screw things up this time around. You see, what I have done is not perhaps what you might expect from a ruthless dictator. I have actually re-empowered the population. This is in stark contrast to what politicians do, which is to progressively rob the public of power.

Before I took over, there were just too many examples of topsy-turvy prioritisation in Britain for society to remain stable and sustainable. Thanks to the efforts of the many pressure groups fronting the politically correct brigade (the PCB) over the last four decades, it had become a country in which far more resources were allocated to looking after the unproductive, parasitic scroungers than to servicing the needs of the average hardworking citizen.

It had become clear to me that the PCB had successfully imposed their will on our society in order to build a gravy train to ride for evermore. By pressurising both government and judiciary to introduce progressively more lenient prison sentences, they ensured that more criminals were created, which in turn helped them to create lucrative jobs for their cronies in the massive 'criminal support' bureaucracies, which once established, they then milked for every penny they could.

The larger these bureaucracies grew, the more power the PCB grabbed for themselves and the more influence they wielded over gutless politicians and the defenceless public. The PCB cunningly pursued sinister agendas disguised as 'enlightened, progressive and humane' policies, entirely for their own benefit.

The height of this insanity culminated when terrorism came to our shores again. When the IRA was in full swing, the PCB were nowhere to be found. That is because there was no money to be made or power to be gained. However, as soon as radical religious minorities became involved, the PCB rubbed their grubby little hands with glee.

Why do you think tens of millions of pounds worth of taxpayers' money was spent defending the rights of radical hate preachers in this country? Well, you only have to work out where all that money went if you want to know. Do you seriously think you could have found a PCB lawyer anywhere who would have believed enough in the rights of one of these hate preachers to defend them for free?

I like to think that by crushing the power of the PCB I have given the power back to the people. I also hope that the incredibly straightforward measures I have taken to remove the hundreds of bureaucratically created frustrations from daily life have proved to the population that they no longer have to accept the nonsense that the power-crazed politicians want to impose upon them.

I never intended to stay in the job for ever; after all, ultimate power corrupts and all that. Of course I believe a civilised country has to be governed democratically. But things had gone too far and a short, sharp dictatorship was all this country needed to set it straight and I knew I was the man for that. However, I will be glad to hand it back to the MPs, frankly, now things are sorted. The day-to-day running of the country is tedious and I need a new challenge.

Might go and have a crack at America – that place needs a serious shaking up for sure.

In my final speech to the population, on the night before the elections, just before I step aboard my private jet to fly off to a secret location where I will lie low for a few years while I plan my next move, I will emphasise the important point that the people should regard politicians as their servants, not their masters.

So Britain is running smoothly now and for the most part the population is much happier, contented and less stressed. I have even received reports that some of those ghastly people who walk around permanently texting on mobiles have been spotted smiling instead of frowning into their phones. Now that has to be some sort of social barometer.

This recording is all about how I went about sorting Britain out, or in my parlance, Got the Job Done (GTJD).

Chapter one

Immigration

I am not against immigrants; they can be good for the country, providing the ones who come contribute to the economy rather than drain it. The problem, of course, is to ensure that you let the right people in, while keeping the wrong ones out. Not easy to achieve even for a dictator. The task requires imagination and daring.

However, before I started to tackle the serious matter of sorting the wheat from the chaff, I decided to deal first with another much less threatening but nevertheless culturally significant type of immigrant.

With regard to this specific group, then, the first measure I took to protect our heritage and our way of life, was to introduce a third customs lane at our ports and airports. In addition to the Nothing to Declare and Goods to Declare lanes there is now an American Girl lane.

This is why. One day a girl in a small country town in the USA wastelands wakes up and realises she is more than averagely attractive and intelligent in comparison to the rest of the women in the town, and through a lucky freak of genetics, weighs fifty pounds less than the lightest of them. In this new state of enlightened self-awareness she looks around at the inbred bearded hillbillies driving around in rusty pick-up trucks through fresh eyes, and says to herself, 'I can do better than to marry one of these retards. I am off to New York to find a better class of man.'

So far, so good. I applaud her ambition but there is one problem. When small-town American girl (STAG) gets to New York, she finds that 70 per cent of the good-looking men would rather sleep with each other than with her. Furthermore, and just as depressingly, the remaining 30 per cent of eligible men have so many women to play with thanks to the other 70 per cent who don't want them, that they are forced to bed two or three at a time just to make any progress at all through the heaving ranks of STAGS like herself arriving daily from the rest of the country on a seemingly endless conveyor belt.

Then one rainy Sunday STAG is consoling herself over this sad state of affairs by going to the cinema with a girlfriend and they happen to watch a film starring either Hugh Grant or Colin Firth or probably both of them at once, and a light bulb goes on in STAG's head. She turns to her friend and says, 'I'm going to go to London to marry a Brit. Everyone knows English girls are always too drunk to be any good in bed, so I will be able to marry whom-ever I want.'

Again, so far, so good, and I admire her resourcefulness and drive even more now, but once again there is a serious flaw in her plan. You see, Americans have absolutely no dress sense whatsoever. I mean zero. And furthermore, unlike any other culture on the planet, they are so brainwashed into believing that the American way is the best way that they cannot adapt to a new environment. The concept of 'when in Rome' does not exist in the American psyche.

So when STAG arrives in London and starts dating the upper-crust Englishmen of her dreams, things don't quite go according to plan.

At first Hooray Henry is bowled over to be going out with a girl with a fit figure and a straight set of teeth, not to mention a voracious sexual appetite and no inhibitions. The problem comes when he first asks her to accompany him to anything vaguely formal. He naively assumes that STAG will know that black tie means a short cocktail dress and heels, rather than the torn designer jeans and sneakers that she turns up in, and that white tie means a ball gown, rather than the bright-red micro mini skirt and plunging cleavage outfit, which she matches with the five-inch heels adorned with enough sequin-covered straps to make a streetwalker envious.

Now Hooray Henry has a serious problem: he has no idea what she will turn up in next, and introducing STAG to Mother is quite out of the question.

Because the Hooray Henrys are too gentlemanly to criticise STAG's outfits, she finds herself repeatedly, if charmingly, dumped by every one of them she dates. At no point does it ever occur to her that to an Englishman, particularly one who is a member of the social stratum she has aimed for, there is nothing so terrible as social embarrassment.

Sadly, after a decade of failing to adapt, she finds herself joining the ranks of the forty-plus-year-old STAGS hanging out together in desperate hunting packs in the middle-age cocktail bars of Chelsea, trying to pick up bald, fat, divorced men with yellow teeth.

This is where my third customs channel comes to the rescue. I have made it my personal business to save the STAGS. It is a waste of good breeding stock for these girls to go unmarried. God knows the country needs some slimmer figures and better teeth in the gene pool, not to mention the entrepreneurial get-up-and-go gutsiness that motivated them to come. It would have been a crime against humanity to let them go to waste.

Breeding with successful invaders has to be a good thing, I say, providing they are attractive and intelligent, of course. That's why the Vikings did so well; just consider our heritage. The ancient Briton women must have been totally awestruck by the sight of these ruggedly handsome, six-foot-tall, blond, muscular invaders with bright-blue eyes, who wrote poems for a hobby when they weren't beheading people with axes.

They must have spent all of ten seconds comparing them with the short, hairy, fat blokes in their village whose only hobbies were brewing foul-tasting beer and competing in who-can-fart-the-loudest competitions, before they thought, *Phwoar, I'm having some of that!* Luckily for them the Vikings were notoriously short-sighted, so it all worked out fine. I believe the question of who-raped-whom is highly debatable, personally.

Anyway, thank God some sex took place, as without the Viking gene injection there wouldn't be any good-looking people in this country at all.

So this is how American Girl lane works: these new lanes are staffed by specially trained, culturally sensitive customs personnel who are alerted by passport control about any American girl arriving with a working visa. They then escort her right through baggage recovery and into American Girl lane and explain that all her clothes must be inspected.

The clothes are then divided into two piles. One will inevitably be a very small pile consisting mostly of underwear and perhaps just a decent pair of designer jeans, maybe even a good pair of shoes if she is lucky; the other much larger pile will consist of the rest of her effects, including make-up. Then her options are explained to her.

If she wishes to enter Britain, all the effects in the larger pile must be sent back to the USA by HM Customs at her expense or donated to charity. She will not have her visa endorsed until she has been accompanied under the escort of a HM Customs licensed taste consultant to purchase suitable clothes at her expense and then receive training in the etiquette relating to the wearing of these outfits to fit in with the high-society lifestyle of the highly eligible men she hopes to date.

Alternatively, if she chooses not to do this, she can save herself ten years of heartache and wasted youth by reclaiming all her belongings and returning to the USA on the next available flight.

In the vast majority of cases the girls have stayed, and I have been reliably informed that a number of notable marriages have resulted, including that of a tall, beautiful and very bright girl from Tennessee who was born in a trailer park and ended up a duchess, having managed to bag herself a handsome young duke.

So, American Girl lane, GTJD.

Other immigrants

You know the problem, because we are members of the European Union, legally we have no option but to accept all EU immigrants, even those from prehistoric countries that use horse manure for currency but that some idiot has nevertheless incorporated into the union. We then have to provide them with warm comfortable homes from which to operate their drug dealing and sex-slave trafficking operations from, while our own pensioners freeze to death in condemned council flats.

We even help to finance these highly lucrative illegal enterprises by paying their entire family the dole and providing free health care.

Well I knew all I needed was a loophole to put a stop to all that. I suspected that somewhere deep inside the Brussels bureaucratic machine there would be a European directive relating to health and safety, and that most likely, as it would be concerned with life and limb preservation, this would through some complex legal machination have precedence over any other laws relating to the movement or transport of people.

The trouble was that none of my EU expert advisors said such a thing was possible to find in the impenetrable archives of Brussels bullshit.

Not to be deterred, I found an Oxford professor who had been formally considered the foremost expert in EU law until he was given a life sentence for murdering his mother-in-law and feeding her body into a branch shredder because he had read somewhere that this was a good way of disposing of a corpse.

Apparently, he only got caught because, being an academic; he was so absent-minded and impractical in nature that he forgot to hose out the shredding machine before returning it to the tool-hire company.

I thought, *Now here is a man I can really motivate*, so I informed him that if he could find me the loophole I needed, I would grant him a full pardon in return for his services to the country. After all, he is hardly a real criminal. I mean, find me a man anywhere who hasn't given serious thought to feeding his mother-in-law into a branch shredder at some time or other.

Sure enough, after a couple of months of ploughing through a paper mountain, he found just the thing.

The Health and Safety loophole

I quickly pushed through a law stating that no EU passport or identity card holders, including British citizens, are allowed to board a plane or train, enter the Channel Tunnel or use a ferry service unless they can read aloud in perfect English, to the satisfaction of the duty transport safety officer (so he can be sure they understand them fully, of course), a set of health and safety regulations relating to that specific method of transport.

These safety regulations are very detailed indeed and extend to at least ten pages. They also contain a lot of unusual phrases, some of which tax the pronunciation capabilities of even most British-born people. However, because there are no exceptions to this requirement, there is no provable prejudice for Brussels to object to.

This minor inconvenience for existing UK citizens was soon accepted as a small price to pay for having Britain back, especially once my new legislation was extended so that every citizen claiming benefits was required to read aloud another set of health and safety regulations relating to their benefit office, which they had to do to the satisfaction of a safety officer on permanent duty in the building before they could enter and make their claim.

This was all the more effective because I put a stop to online and telephone claims on the basis that every claimant's identity must be checked at the point of making a claim to prevent fraud.

Because this new, yet obviously 'essential', health and safety requirement was imposed on all claimants entering benefit offices, irrespective of race, Brussels was again unable to prove prejudice and block the move. In addition, by a remarkable feat of draughtsman-ship, my tame Oxford professor managed to extend this document to twenty-seven pages and ensure it contained even more complex phraseology than the transport document.

Dangerous places benefits offices, you know. As I pointed out to Brussels, most of them are old and in a poor state of repair; anything could happen in one, couldn't it?

The 99.7 per cent of immigrant claimants who failed to read the health and safety regulations aloud to the satisfaction of the health and safety officer posted in every benefits office, soon left the country of their own accord at no cost to the taxpayer.

An unexpected bonus was that most of the 46.3 per cent of British nationals who could not read the regulations either also left to claim benefit in other EU countries like France and Belgium.

Problem solved, then! The Health and Safety loophole, GTJD.

Chapter two

Taxation

This is the thing about taxation: every single politician in the world knows how to solve the problem of tax but none of them have the guts to implement it. It is very simple – if you tax the rich only a little, you don't have to tax the poor at all.

The reason no politician dares to do this is that sadly the whole business of taxation in the world of politics is mixed up with a left-wing social agenda based on envy, which has nothing to do with the actual practical process of tax collection.

Conventional political wisdom is that the rich should pay more tax than the ordinary citizen because they are obviously crooks or evil, exploitative bastards who have made their money off the sweat of honest working people.

We all know this is total nonsense of course, but it has been reinforced so much through political history that even modern politicians still fear that suggesting the obvious solution to taxation would appear totally unacceptable to the electorate.

The pinnacle of this lefty insanity came when the laughably ridiculous, almost Monty Pythonesque Labour Party of the mid 1970s imposed 75 per cent taxation on the rich. This policy directly caused the brain drain of the 1970s, as all the high-earners – the most productive and intelligent people in Britain – left, setting the whole country back decades and causing mass unemployment and misery for the working class whose interests these hypocritical lefty loonies claimed to be protecting.

But still, due to this traditional and deep-seated political view of taxation, even decades later in the twenty-first century, all the gutless politicians could do before I took over was to bodge up ill-conceived tax systems that hurt the poor and irritated the middle classes, but which were completely avoided by the rich, who simply lived elsewhere.

Thanks to this totally bonkers socialist attitude, the whole tax business was topsy-turvy. Let's think about it objectively: firstly, even if the rich *were* paying tax at the basic rate, they would *already* be paying more tax than anyone else because as an individual they would end up making an infinitely larger contribution to the Treasury than an average person.

Secondly, in all other aspects of life, if you buy in bulk you get a discount, not a higher cost. So, actually it should have been the other way around; the rich should have been asked to pay a lower rate of tax, not a higher one.

Take Monaco for example. Because the rich pay a very reasonable rate of tax, they are happy to use the place as their tax residence and consequently there is so much money in the pot that no waiter, croupier or road sweeper has to pay any tax at all. Furthermore because the principality can afford it, the ordinary working population are provided with free health care in private hospitals and live rent free for life in spacious council flats overlooking the harbour, which would cost anyone else £5 million a year to lease.

Try suggesting to any of those Monaco workers that the tax rate should go up for the rich and they will turn pale with fear because they know if that happened the rich would leave and they would have to start paying tax themselves to make up for the shortfall.

Common-sense tax system

Right, so this is the tax regime I introduced as soon as I took over: the average wage in this country is currently around £32,000. My tax system ensures that no one has to pay any tax on earnings up to

£50,000; after that they pay a 10 per cent flat rate right up to a million. Earnings of married couples are not amalgamated.

How could I afford do this? Simple – because I offered the super rich a 10 per cent flat rate of tax on the first £950,000 of earnings, after which the rate drops 1 per cent per million to a base-rate minimum of 5 per cent.

I knew we did not have to offer the lowest tax rate in the world to get the super rich to change their tax residences to Britain, just a reasonable one. This is because unlike soulless little dumps like Monaco and Reno, we are a proper country and have London, the most desirable capital city in the world to live in, and because, as I have said before, we are most sensible, civilised dependable race on the planet, so everyone feels safe living here.

Most tax havens like Monaco are packed full of dodgy people you wouldn't invite around for dinner, whereas London is packed full of fascinating cultured people. So if you have to make the choice between an Algerian gun-runner or someone like Dan Cruickshank for your next-door neighbour, which are you going to pick? No contest, you would think sod the odd extra couple of per cent of tax and come to live in London, wouldn't you?

Plus, as a bonus, there is no chance of becoming collateral damage in a drive-by shooting when you are putting out the bins.

By the end of the second year of my being in power, the tax revenues pouring in had grown to the highest ever recorded by the Treasury. By the end of year three, they were almost 45 per cent higher than the year before I took over. This was achieved despite 80 per cent of the population paying no income tax whatsoever.

The majority of the super rich who fill the Treasury coffers spent less than a third of the year actually in Britain, but even in their absence, they spend astronomical sums employing British craftsman to remodel their expansive homes and to customise yachts, private jets and cars for them, creating jobs and putting even more money into our economy.

I introduced another incentive for the international super rich, too, a programme called Adopt a Building. It works like this.

Adopt a Building

If one of the international super rich wishes, they can receive a permanent reduction of 1 per cent on their base tax rate, from 5 per cent to 4 per cent, in return for paying for the redevelopment of a block of rundown council flats into high-grade modern accommodation.

To achieve this, they pay for the residents to be temporarily rehoused, or sent abroad on holiday if they are pensioners (which ironically often works out cheaper, especially as several enthusiastic package holiday companies have become linked to the programme).

With the residents out of the way, the entire building is either stripped out or demolished and then rebuilt to a very high standard. When finished, the building is then dedicated to the person who paid for it, and he or she is offered full British citizenship in addition to the tax break.

If a super-wealthy type is prepared to fund the restoration of ten such buildings, they are, in addition, offered an OBE. If they fund the restoration of a hundred buildings, an investment probably representing at least half a billion pounds, they get a knighthood.

The program has proved very successful. From the outset, I made sure that blocks of flats with the largest proportion of pensioners were prioritised, as the third-world conditions in which many of them lived were a disgrace and brought shame on a country of our standing.

The fact that before I took over, successive governments of all political persuasions sent billions abroad in aid to other countries rather than sorting out our own disadvantaged people is just another reason I despise politicians and the hypocritical PCB lefties so much.

When I banished the MPs to work on the railways in Canada, I insisted that they were all to spend five years living in the same conditions as so many of our own poor used to before I took over and started to do something about it.

When they get back, it will be interesting to hear how the MPs liked living like that. Maybe they will now appreciate the merit in the old adage charity begins at home.

By engaging the services of the best cityscape architects, many of the rundown inner-city estates throughout the land have now been completely turned around under the Adopt a Building program, and are quite unrecognisable from their original state.

Wherever practical, ornamental gardens and play areas for children have been incorporated into the space between buildings, along with pedestrian-only spaces to reduce stress and improve quality of life.

Some architects claim that it is possible to 'design crime out' of an urban environment. I do not know if this is true, but I certainly know that people treat each other better if they are living in a more aesthetically pleasing and less stressful environment.

So far twenty-six OBEs and nine knighthoods have been awarded. I consider them good value for what the residents of these buildings have received in return. After all, why not? I would rather give a knighthood to someone who has transformed the lives of hundreds of people for the better than for financially backing a particular political party, which is why a lot of them have been handed out over the years.

The honours system might be old fashioned, but by God it still has a lot of relevance and clout if used wisely.

A lot of these super-wealthy types secretly feel a bit guilty about their luck. All they need is an opportunity to make a serious practical contribution that they can see and touch in good old bricks and mortar, while at the same time letting them get a serious ego boost out of an knighthood that they can impress their friends with. Not only that, but a lot of them, like the Russian oligarchs, were brought up in soul-destroying dumps as kids themselves, so it is something they can really relate to.

I met such a man recently at a reception in 10 Downing Street after he picked up his knighthood at Buckingham Palace. He was a Russian oil billionaire. He grabbed my right hand in both of his and, with his eyes wet with tears and his voice choked with feeling, he thanked me for creating a programme that made him feel like he had freed other people from a living hell like the one he grew up in. He was a rough diamond and a hard, ruthless-looking man with a broken nose and hands as rough as sandpaper, but his emotion was so utterly genuine that I was really quite moved, and it made a great front-page picture for the newspapers the next day, too.

I have said it before – the respect held by foreigners for our well-balanced and even-handed character, and particularly for our quirky old traditions, is still much greater than most British people believe. Enough certainly, it turns out, for a foreign tycoon to be prepared to spend half a billion to get a knighthood.

You can be damn sure they would not pay that to get a German, French or Italian title. That is the point, you see – only a British one counts. Even in the hedonistic high-flying world of private jets and yachts inhabited by the world's billionaires, there is no clearer way of demonstrating one-upmanship than a British title.

To me, it is just another example of Britain's unique status in the world. We command respect and admiration from foreigners, so why not use it to do some good for those less fortunate members of our population who need a break?

Predictably my new tax regime caused a knee-jerk reaction from the loony left, who started banging on about the social unjustness of the rich getting away with paying so little tax. But to their surprise and annoyance, they received absolutely no support from the public whatsoever, the vast majority of whom were, as I had expected, far more interested in their new tax-free status and were busy looking around car showrooms and home-improvement stores, or, in the case of the council-flat pensioners, enjoying returning home to nicely decorated, modern, centrally heated apartments instead of having to stop on the way to collect a dozen free newspapers to wrap themselves in just to stay alive until morning.

Common-sense tax system and Adopt a Building, both of them GTJD.

Chapter three

The Environment

So here is a question: take a modern, politically correct hybrid electric car and a new Ferrari V12 Berlinetta. Which do you think has the worse impact on the environment over 100,000 miles?

If you guessed that the hybrid is the bad boy, then you guessed right, but I expect if you got that wrong, you would like to know why.

Well you see when the scientifically ignorant Primrose Hill-dwelling, herbal-tea-quaffing, Al Gore-brainwashed, so-much-holier-than-thou brigade rushed out to buy their stupid hybrids, they forgot to do their homework first.

This is because the amount of CO_2 a vehicle creates in its life has nothing like as much negative impact on the earth's natural resources and Mother Nature's well-being in general as *how* and *where* it is made.

Hybrids and electric cars are mass-produced vehicles, which are mostly just another cynical product range of irresponsible global conglomerates who couldn't give a rat's arse about the environment but do care about making money out of well-meaning suckers who do.

Take your typical hybrid buyer, the sandal-wearing Tarquin, a forty-three-year-old sociology teacher from East Grimstead who apologises to carrots before he eats them raw. What Tarquin doesn't realise is that the components for these hypocritical vehicles travel back and forth across the globe so many times just to build a car for him to feel smug driving around in, that by the time the bloody thing has finally been manufactured, the international transportation involved has produced so much CO_2 he might as well commute to work in an 7-litre AC Cobra.

In one case I believe that real environmental scientists (a very rare breed, there are very few genuine environmental scientists with enough integrity not to be riding on Al's gravy train. I think there are only about five of them in the entire world) have identified that the battery components alone in one popular contemporary hybrid travel across the globe four times before being installed in the final product, which, as a complete car, is then itself transported for thousands of miles to the other side of the world to find its very own Tarquin to love it.

In addition to this, hybrids require a lot of rare earth elements, stuff which ends in *-ium*, like lithium. These elements are for the main part only mined in parts of the world like China, where health and safety does not exist and life is cheaper than a bag of crisps. People mining rare earth elements have a shorter life expectancy than a household fly.

So not only should Tarquin stop feeling so smug about his pointless hybrid but he should also consider that he is certainly partly responsible for the death of at least one Chinese miner and the subsequent starvation of his wife and children.

Not only that, but Tarquin should also ponder on the staggering fact that in order to rip enough *-ium* stuff from the bosom of Mother Gaia to construct his mobile ego massager, a hole the size of a four-bedroom house has been left by a massive 65,000cc, 2300-horsepower earth mover that belched out enough CO_2 per second from its clapped-out uncatalysed exhaust to power a small city.

The reality is that the damage done to the environment in order to mine the rare earth materials needed for hybrid cars is irreversible and catastrophic. It permanently destroys millions of square acres of agricultural land and does infinitely more long-term harm to the environment than a conventional car does by burning a little bit of petrol.

Even the normally tight-lipped Chinese government is so concerned about the damage caused by this heinous activity that a regulator at its Ministry of Technology recently made a ground-breaking statement to the *New York Times*: 'This rare earth mining [for hybrid car construction] has caused great harm to ecology and the environment.'

For the Chinese to publically state that, it really has to be catastrophically serious. They normally wouldn't admit anything even if the country ran out of rice.

The reality is that hybrid manufacturers have done their market research very thoroughly. They realise that due to the decline in educational standards throughout the Western world (in our case thanks to the influence of the PCB who don't want schoolchildren to learn anything as hard as science in case the lowest common dominator, i.e. the thickest child in any class, can't manage it), 99 per cent of the population are scientifically ignorant.

If this wasn't true, the cynical hybrid manufacturers could never get away with selling these vehicles. It is no coincidence that hybrids are very seldom owned by well-educated people. None of my contemporaries with science degrees from Cambridge would be seen dead in one, for instance. In contrast just look at how many vacuous Hollywood stars smugly drive around in hybrids to massage their egos.

Hybrids are just window dressing. All joking aside, Tarquin literally would be more ecologically responsible to drive an AC Cobra to work. At least it was constructed by hand out of natural sustainable materials like wood, aluminium, leather and cast iron. Furthermore, it wouldn't even recognise a bit of *-ium* even if it drove over it. The fact it only does fourteen miles to the gallon is irrelevant.

Not so smug now are you Tarquin? If you had spent a bit more time studying science instead of the dubious activities of Willmot and Young, you might realise you have been well and truly suckered, my old sandal-totting carrot-chomper.

Real ecologically sound manufacturing

Now if you want to see how to build a car responsibly, or build anything with multiple components responsibly, you should pay a visit to the most genuinely ecologically sound factory in the world, winner of the Best Place To Work in Europe award: the Ferrari factory.

Old man Enzo knew a thing or two about recycling and taking care of resources. He had to because at the end of the World War II there weren't any at all, and that was not very useful for a man who dreamt of building the best racing cars in the world.

At the end of World War II, due to rationing restrictions, no Italian manufacturer was allowed a piece of sheet steel larger than a pocket handkerchief, about eight inches square. Enzo got around that by getting his men to seam weld hundreds of them into larger sheets and then hand beat them into beautiful body panels over lumps of carved hard wood in the shape of the body part. Even the most expensive classic Ferrari, now changing hands for around £15 million, the beautiful 250 GTO, was still produced like this as late as the 1960s, which is why no two are exactly the same.

During that immediate post-war period, no manufacturer was allowed any metal to build engines either, so Enzo sent men around on horses and carts to collect up bits of discarded military vehicles and munitions at the sides of the road and in fields and hedgerows.

Then by dint of employing the descendants of the finest metal workers in the world, the Etruscans, whose ancestors had moved to the Italian Alps many centuries earlier and whose innate metallurgy skills defy scientific explanation, Enzo forged these exotic alloy combinations of military scrap into a tiny 1.5 litre V12 engine.

When he fired it up for the first time, in the spring of 1947, the world awoke to hear a noise it wouldn't forget for the rest of time, the spine-tingling howl of a high-revving Ferrari V12, the battle cry of Italy that would go on to scream its defiance and deadly intent across the world's racing circuits for decades to come and is still doing so to this day.

The most remarkable thing about this groundbreaking car, the 125 as it was called, was not just the fact that it was far more advanced than anything seen before but that every single component had been bartered for, begged for or collected as scrap from the surrounding countryside by the Italian version of Steptoe and Son.

When you start out like that, you learn to appreciate resources and the need to do things highly efficiently, thoughtfully and responsibly.

Whereas car-building conglomerates will source components on the basis of cost from anywhere on the planet, Ferrari sources the majority of its vehicle components and raw materials locally rather from abroad. That's truly green, Tarquin.

Because unlike other manufacturers who source an engine from one country and a chassis from another, Ferrari still forge, yes *forge* their own engines on site. This means that whereas a certain size of lorry might carry one hundred ordinary car or hybrid engines, the same lorry can carry enough alloy billets to forge 10,000 Ferrari engines on site. That is a hundred times more ecologically responsible.

Hello, Tarquin, are we learning yet?

Ferrari has been a net producer of electricity for the Italian grid for over fifty years. Because until very recently the Italian grid produced massive voltage fluctuations, which made precision welding difficult, Ferrari came up with the idea of using their engine test room to generate electricity much more consistently. With six or more massively powerful engines being bedded in at any one time, they soon had a surplus to sell to the grid.

Do you know of any other car manufacturer that has been generating electricity for fifty years, Tarquin? Any hybrid manufacturers perhaps? Before they jumped on the lucrative environmental bandwagon and were still building conventional cars? That will be a no then. Incidentally, by successfully reducing its CO_2 emissions by 40 per cent, the Ferrari factory is also one of the few factories in the world that met the targets of the Kyoto protocol ten years ahead of schedule.

Most of the Ferrari workforce can cycle the short commute to their homes if they want because most of them live within a very short distance of the factory, some within walking distance. Those living only slightly further away, ride mopeds, which do 250 miles to the gallon, or electric cycles, which can be charged at the factory.

That's the benefit of having an ecologically sound recruitment and training policy, where instead of filling the roads with long-distance commuters because it's cheaper to build a factory in the middle of nowhere like every other car manufacturer on the planet, including those producing hybrids, Ferrari keep their factory where it has always been, in the middle of where their workforce lives. *Duh.*

Oh, and by the way, for the benefit of the PCB I must tell you that there are nearly as many women working there as men and there is no ageism. It is a family atmosphere where one can see three generations of the same family working happily together, from grandma sewing the seats right through to her grandson building the engines. Ferrari likes continuity; it breeds a sense of family pride and ownership into the workforce.

Ferrari also looks after the welfare of its workforce better than any other employer on the planet, providing an extremely high standard of private health care and preventative medical treatment to ensure their workforce remains healthy and happy. In the interests of creating a low-stress working environment, they have gone so far as to build a beautiful piazza in the centre of the factory, with gardens, water fountains and trees, where the workforce can relax during the lunch break. It even has a shop, a coffee bar and a restaurant.

Tarquin, are you listening? This is the way you do it, not by buying a politically correct car that makes you feel good about yourself but in reality is actually destroying the earth and killing exploited Chinese miners while it is doing it.

My manufacturing policy

Hardly surprisingly I have used the case study of the Ferrari factory to create a manufacturing policy for Britain and arranged for leaders of industry to visit it and study it.

Grants are now available to assist manufacturers to become more efficient and become genuinely ecologically sound rather than having to pretend to be for the purposes of political correctness.

Sometimes this involves doing things that, to the ignorant like Tarquin, might look ecologically unsound, such as creating on-site forges, but which in reality massively reduce the overall impact of component transport on the greater environment.

The electric vehicle challenge

We could build short-range electric vehicles here in Britain without creating some of the negative impacts of the current ones just through responsible manufacture – by building them in just one place, Ferrari style, and by utilising only recycled battery materials rather than ripping any more *-ium* out of the earth. Their charge would not last so long but for short-range urban use they would be practical. There is, however, a bigger problem.

Most of our electricity is still generated by dirty old coal-fired power stations, so electric cars are doing nothing for the broader environment in Britain.

Don't get me wrong, electric vehicles can help to clean up the local environment, which is certainly welcome in a city and makes it a more pleasant place to live and work, but all they are otherwise doing is displacing that CO_2 pollution to the smoky old coal-fired power station down the road.

Electric cars are all the rage in California because all the electricity there is generated by nuclear power stations, and so there is a genuine net reduction of CO_2 in the broader environment during the operational life of the vehicle. The only minor technical problem is that some bright spark built some of the biggest nuclear power stations right on the San Andreas Fault, so when it wakes up one day in a particularly bad mood, the whole of the west coast of America will be blown two hundred miles into the Pacific. Oh well, as my old gran used to say, every cloud has a silver lining.

Changing the time in winter

Britain is now a much lighter happier place in winter. This is because I put an end to the ludicrous tradition of setting the clocks back an hour in late October.

I never understood why the clocks were put back in winter in the first place; to me this was utterly illogical. I always felt that instead they should always have gone forward an hour to maximise the available daytime hours. Well I am glad to say that is what they now do, to the great delight of the vast majority of the population.

However, before I altered the status quo, I did some in-depth research just in case I was missing something important.

I used to believe that it all started in World War II but in fact, having looked into the history, it transpires that we very sensibly did the exact opposite during the war years. Between 1940 and 1945, and also in 1947, we actually switched to British Double Summer Time (BDST). Why? We did so to save precious fuel as it was in limited supply. That *should* have struck a chord today with the green brigade, don't you think?

You bet it *should* have. Supporters of BDST, including a couple of the five real environmental scientists in the world, have pointed out for over a decade that 500,000 tonnes of CO_2 would be saved every year, if instead of putting the clocks back we put them forward one hour further in the spring, thereby achieving British Double Summer Time (BDST).

Half a million tonnes of CO_2 is the equivalent of permanently removing 18 million motor vehicles from the road; in other words half of the vehicles in the country.

Why did the eco-warriors like Tarquin keep so quiet about this? They were meant to be concerned about the environment, surely they should have been screaming from the rooftops about CO_2 savings like this? This level of serious CO_2 reduction made all their bleating about wind turbines and solar panels seem stupid. Unlike these 'alternative' and supposedly 'sustainable' energy sources, which we all know can only be viable thanks to taxpayer subsidies, putting the clocks forward is free, and you can't get anything greener than a free CO_2 reduction.

Strangely, despite these incredible potential CO_2 savings, there was barely a whisper from what is normally the most vocal section of the green orchestra. Now I am no conspiracy theorist but I cannot help but feel that this was highly odd if not downright suspicious. I smell a political agenda courtesy of the loony left and the PCB.

There have always been myths concerning BDST, including loud if ill-defined references to farming being the reason for us being plunged into darkness earlier than necessary. This is something that, as a man brought up in the countryside, I have always found puzzling.

Farmers do not rely on the time indicated on their watches to go about their business. They do what their ancestors have done for thousands of years: they operate from first light to last light. Where that time happens to be recorded on a watch face is all but irrelevant to them because, unlike 90 per cent of the population, they do not have to catch trains or commute to work.

What's more, cows don't wear watches, they just know when they want to be milked and they don't care what Mr Rolex has to say about it.

Interestingly, though, even this well-worn excuse to leave things as they were, actually held no water. My researchers discovered that in March 2010, in a survey of their membership, the National Farmers Union found that most respondent farmers wanted more, not less evening daylight in winter.

Another long-term excuse was that children in the north of Britain would be in more danger walking to school in the mornings if it were dark. Walking to school? When was the last time a kid walked to school in this country, 1971?

My research team found out that the Royal Society for the Prevention of Accidents (RoSPA), the RAC and the AA had campaigned for years to reintroduce BDST as they claimed that police accident records clearly indicate that more accidents occur in the dark evenings during rush hour, when tired commuters are returning from work than occur when they are commuting in the mornings. According to their combined research, they estimated six hundred lives per year could be saved.

Six hundred lives. That's the equivalent of a bloody massacre. It is common sense though; the evening commuting hour is the time of day when the largest proportion of fatal accidents occur. If you can keep this time of the day as light as possible, you are bound to reduce accidents.

While successive governments of all parties have ignored their pleas over the decades, in contrast I very much listened to them. Not that I needed convincing when all the other benefits of doing away with this ridiculously outdated concept were taken into consideration.

So on the twenty-sixth of the first October after I came into power, I stopped the ridiculous business of the clocks going back and instead put them forward one hour on the first of November, giving an extra hour of light for the vast majority of the country.

I reasoned that if the experts found that Double Summer Time, based on an extra hour in summer, saved 600 lives and 500,000 tonnes of CO_2, then if instead of waiting until spring to put the clocks forward we did this on 1 November and kept it there for five months until the last day of March, we would save even more of both.

After all, British summertime doesn't need the extra hour, it is light from 4.30 a.m. to 10.30 p.m. How can you beat that? No, I gambled that it would far more beneficial if the extra hour was in the wintertime so that even on the shortest day, for 85 per cent of the population, darkness would not fall before 6 p.m.

This gamble has paid off big time. The road-accident records now indicate a net average of nearly 720 fewer fatal accidents per year since the change. Also, an audit of all the country's energy companies' records indicate an average annual saving of over 650,000 tonnes of CO_2. Equivalent to the CO_2 produced by nearly 65 per cent of all cars in Britain in a year.

So, putting the clocks one hour forward in winter instead of one hour back, GTJD.

Christmas lights

The annoying practice of putting up Christmas lights in town and city centres in mid October creates a massive and quite unnecessary consumption of energy throughout the land. I passed a law that Christmas lights cannot now be installed in public places earlier than 1 December and that they must be switched off by 2 January and removed by 5 January.

Fracking

Fracking has got itself a bad name because some cowboy operators in the wild west of America, where no regulations exist, took short cuts, as usual. Side effects of their irresponsible behaviour such as flames coming out of taps instead of water, were purely due to the fracking activities of people with fewer morals than a Vegas hooker.

My Oxbridge scientists assured me that fracking can in fact be done without discernable environmental impact and without the deployment of any dangerous chemicals. Apparently they have perfected a way of extracting shale oil and gas through the deployment of a combination of ultrasound and pure natural water. They claim that if we did it, we could make enough money to pay off the national debt in less than a year.

I called a meeting of all the top scientific experts on both sides to 10 Downing Street to discuss the pros and cons of fracking in depth. After an hour of listening to their ultra-dull tech speak, much of which was going well over my head, I turned to my chancellor of the exchequer and said, 'OK, enough of this scientific crap, just give me the bottom line in English please.'

He took a long, deep breath and replied, 'Well, if we decide only to frack in the remotest areas where no one even ever goes, apart from one particular bearded guy in an anorak who we can either pay off or push into a bog, and then even if we do it *so* sensitively that no one can see our fracking sites even from the air, because we plant a wood of fully grown mature trees around each site, at £2,000 a tree, and then *even* if we pay every local person within five square miles a million quid each to go somewhere else or shut up, and *even* if we operate the most ecologically sensitive fracking operation in the world including rehousing each hedgehog in its own personal Wimpy home … we can still pay the national debt off in nine months and then pay off everybody's mortgages in another three, and then still have enough money over to give every family in the land a new car each for Christmas.'

I replied, 'Thanks, gents. Now stop talking and get fracking. We need a new Royal Navy.'

Chapter four

Business and Innovation

When I was seventeen I owned an ancient Triumph 500cc motorbike. Sometimes this seems like yesterday and sometimes it seems such a long time ago that my memories of that period in my life are like watching a film about someone else entirely. The bike was an old clapped-out 1964 Tiger100 SS, which consumed as much oil as it did petrol. Not only did its worn-out pistons pass vast quantities of oil, but it also leaked so much from its equally worn crankcase gaskets that I had to carry a packet of chewing gum around in its capacious tool roll just to stop up the worst leaks and prevent it from shuddering to an abrupt halt from a seizure.

At that time teenagers were not the brainwashed brand ambassadors that they are today, obsessing over which type of sneakers or jeans to wear. In those days I would not have understood what a clothes brand meant. Clothes were the last thing on my mind; they were just things that kept you warm, and if they were made of waxed cotton like a Belstaff jacket, maybe even dry.

There were only two things a red-blooded male teenager like myself ever thought about at all: how to get a bigger motorbike than the one you already had and how to get laid as often as possible. It did not matter if you were born on a council estate or in a crumbling manor house on a seven-hundred-acre estate, as I was; the ambitions were exactly the same.

In the mind of a seventeen-year-old, there was a direct correlation between these two things. The bigger the bike, the more girls would want to ride on the back, and the more girls you carried on the pillion, the more chances there were to get laid. God, life really was just so simple then. If only it were possible to remain seventeen for ever.

However, there was just one small fly in the ointment. Because there were never any spare parts available for the old Triumph, it only worked occasionally, and even then, not for very long. In this sense it often acted more effectively as a noisy contraception device than as a means of transport.

The nearest Triumph dealership was situated in a sprawling single-storey stone building, which had once served as a warehouse when the city in which it was located had boasted a busy wharf. The large warehouse doors at the front of the building had been replaced by floor-to-ceiling glass panels, behind which a shabby showroom was to be found. In this once-grand but now rundown display area sat a new example of each of the three current Triumph 750 models, each lolling lazily on its side stand and steadily dripping oil onto the sawdust-covered wooden floor.

These three models based around the T140, comprising the UK spec and USA spec Bonneville and the Tiger 750, represented the last holdouts of what was once the largest motorcycle industry in the world. They were still being produced in sporadic dribs and drabs during the dying years of the Triumph factory at Meriden, which by this time operated as a workers' cooperative.

Other than these new bikes, there would be a couple of second-hand Triumphs and perhaps occasionally one of the last Norton Commandos, which, being the largest capacity British bike produced at that time at 850cc, represented the ultimate two-wheel fantasy machine for an awestruck teenager.

At the far end of the showroom there was a wooden door stained by oily handprints, which had the word PARTS glued to it in individual capital registration-plate letters. This led through into a long, dark, narrow passage, at the end of which was another equally filthy door. Once you pushed through this, you found yourself in a cavernous warehouse with a domed ceiling. A crudely constructed stud wall separated a small reception area in front from the parts warehousing area behind, which was hidden from view.

The fact that it never seemed to contain any customers when-ever I went there would have been a clue to anyone but a naive seventeen-year-old.

In front of the stud-wall partition was a dusty wooden counter, behind which stood a bored-looking, middle-aged man with thinning hair and spectacles, wearing a brown coat. His face was permanently etched with the expression of one who had long ago given up on life.

As soon as he saw me push through the second door at the end of the passage, his gaze would instantly flick upwards to an oil stain on the ceiling above him, and there it would remain locked in a fascinated stare, as if it was the first time he had ever noticed it, which I knew was not the case as he had done exactly the same thing on every previous occasion I had visited him.

He would stay frozen in this position while studiously ignoring my presence and remain staring at the ceiling in total silence for at least ninety seconds. I knew it was for at least this long because after the third visit I had started to time this curious behaviour with the stopwatch function on my wristwatch. I also knew it was pointless to attempt to interrupt this ritual, so I would wait there in patient silence, breathing in the unique aroma of stale Castrol oil, tobacco smoke and sawdust.

I suppose the fact that an oil stain had managed to manifest itself in the centre of the eleven or twelve-foot-high domed ceiling, while not actually miraculous in the spiritual sense, was nevertheless quite an unusual occurrence even for a Triumph dealership. I have to admit that on most occasions, as I stood there in respectful silence, I found myself speculating on the level of mechanical disaster necessary for a jet of oil to defy gravity sufficiently to reach that high. This mild intellectual exercise helped to pass the time while waiting for Mr Brown Coat to rejoin the human race.

Once he felt a sufficient period had elapsed to establish the importance of his station in life, and his potential influence on mine, he always ended the ceremony of the ceiling worship in exactly the same way. First he would let out a small sigh, as if to indicate that, as had been the case on all previous occasions, this particular staring session had failed to reveal the mystery of the oil stain to him. Then he would reluctantly tear his gaze away from it

31

and, without looking in my direction at all, he would suddenly snap out in an unnecessarily sharp manner only two words: 'Yes, mate?' Not, you will note, 'Good morning, sir, and how may we help you today?' Or anything of that kind, just a loud, short and sharp 'Yes, mate?'

This was my cue to produce a dog-eared scrap of folded paper with a list of motorbike parts scrawled on it in biro from the depths of my grubby biker-jacket pocket and to read out the first item. This action would then trigger the second well-established ritual, which commenced with another sigh from Mr Brown Coat, but longer and deeper this time, followed by the opening of one of four very large and well-thumbed Triumph parts catalogues, which were secured to the desk by short lengths of stainless-steel dog chain. Although the rest of the automotive industry had computerised their spare parts supply years ago, Triumph had not yet caught up.

Each of the four catalogues related to a particular model series of Triumph motorbike and contained beautifully detailed hand-drawn exploded illustrations of the various major mechanical groups such as the crank group and the gearbox group and so forth. These catalogues were works of art in their own right and I always wondered where Triumph found the draughtsman to create these wonderful technical drawings, which were as exquisitely accurate in every minute detail as any of the works of Michelangelo. It was hardly surprising that they were chained down.

Mr Brown Coat would then locate the appropriate page in the book and slowly and deliberately run his nicotine-stained fingers down the lines of part numbers until he identified the appropriate component. This process, when completed, triggered the third ritual, which was preceded by an even deeper sigh than the one which foretold the second. At this point he would turn, once again in the slow and deliberate manner of a man who realises there is no point in rushing things, to a dust-covered microfiche reader and then cross reference this part number against his stock holding.

After about two or sometimes even three minutes of total silence, he would quite suddenly announce, again in an unnecessarily loud and sharp tone, 'On back order, mate,' as he slammed the catalogue shut with an air of finality that, as it turns out, correctly hinted that this situation was unlikely to change in the foreseeable future.

Having then allowed precisely four seconds for dramatic effect, just to ensure that this piece of devastating news had sufficiently sunk in, he followed it with a sharp 'Anyfink else, mate?'

The laborious processes of the second and third rituals were faithfully repeated over and over as I worked my way down through my extensive wish list one item at a time, which usually took about half an hour. Apart from the very occasional curt request for confirmation of some technical detail, Mr Brown Coat's only vocal interactions with me were based around his three stock phrases, 'Yes, mate?', 'On back order, mate' and 'Anyfink else, mate?' He was a man of very few words; for instance, he never greeted me or said goodbye.

I always left empty handed, because not once did Mr Brown Coat manage to find a single part that wasn't on back order. Despite this, with the inherit optimism of a seventeen-year-old, I would return week after week in the hopes that something on my list might have turned up to improve the reliability of my Triumph and therefore by extension, of my love life. Alas, though, this never happened.

Then one day while I was engaged in the third ritual with Mr Brown Coat for the fourth or fifth time that particular morning, something unusual happened. The telephone rang, its strident and insistent tone shattering the cathedral-like silence of the dimly lit and dusty cavern. Mr Brown Coat nearly jumped out of his skin and he stared in angry disbelief at the filthy oil-impregnated, black Bakelite instrument, a relic of the late sixties, which, like everything else in the shop, had never been replaced.

After about thirty seconds of violent ringing, the ancient instrument appeared to break free from the grip of a dried-up puddle of spilt sugary coffee, which had moored it firmly in place since the last time it had been awoken from a long slumber, and started performing an impatient little circular dance on the counter top. Mr Brown Coat, with his frowning face still displaying an expression that successfully combined annoyance and suspicious disbelief, gingerly reached over with a fully extended arm and picked up the receiver as if he were handling an unexploded anti-personnel mine.

Soon he was deep in conversation with what I can only imagine was the Triumph factory. Perhaps they had found a spare part somewhere while spring-cleaning. Anyway, I realised that this unusual event had provided me with an opportunity, which was unlikely to occur again.

Mr Brown Coat's back was turned to me as he irritatedly fiddled with the microfiche machine. I seized my chance and slipped silently under the counter's entry gap without raising the hinged top and with a pounding heart entered the dimly lit gloom of the domed warehouse behind.

The sight that greeted me was enough to shock a trusting teenager to the core. Apart from a dozen or so faded cardboard boxes containing Lucas headlamp bulbs, the rows of dusty shelves were all empty, row upon row stretching into the darkness beyond. Despite my sense of horror, curiosity got the better of me and I swiftly ran further into the warehouse, desperately casting left and right in the hope that the dark recesses might reveal hidden treasures. But the shelves were all empty.

There simply were no spare parts, and clearly there had not been any for some considerable time. Mr Brown Coat had being lying to me from the first time I entered the building some five months earlier. The three rituals were just part of a sadistic game he had invented to inject some light relief into his pointless working day, possibly to prevent him going insane, or because he already had.

I slipped silently out past Mr Brown Coat and ran back down the gloomy passage to the showroom, never to return again, my illusions shattered by the discovery that there never had been any parts coming and that his very job was a sham. It was no more than window dressing for a desperate British motorcycle dealership trying to create the illusion that the game was not over. In doing so, it was merely reflecting the state of the rest of the industry, itself also desperately holding on for a miracle that never seemed to come.

Somehow the Triumph dealership and Mr Brown Coat managed to keep the act up for nearly two more years until one day they suddenly disappeared and the warehouse was turned into a gay nightclub.

By the eighties the British motorcycle industry, which had once been the largest and most respected in the world, came so close to total extinction that it was nearly snuffed out for good. Then one day a man came along who singlehandedly saved it. He was a multimillionaire house builder called John Bloor who bought the Triumph brand from the receivers in 1983 and, once his engineering design team had developed and tested a totally new range of Triumph motorcycle models, invested £80 million of his own money in 1991 to build a brand-new factory at Hinckley in Leicestershire in order to manufacture them.

Since then, year-on-year sales growth has transformed a defunct brand into one of the most successful motorcycle manufacturers of all time, with a turnover of £368 million and worldwide sales of 52,000 bikes per annum. Bikes that are at least as technologically advanced as the Japanese models and that are respected for their durability and bulletproof reliability by motorcyclists throughout the world. Bikes that have increasingly become the first choice of professional international motorcycle adventure tour guides, not for reasons of sentimentality but because they have proved more reliable and capable than the competing Japanese and German brands.

Despite having my illusions shattered as a teenager, what I came to appreciate from the example of Triumph motorcycles is that no matter how dire the odds are or how desperate or apparently hopeless the situation or how lost the cause, all it takes to turn it all around is one well-motivated man with belief in the abilities of his fellow countrymen and access to sufficient financial resources.

One could almost say that the story of my teenage experience and the subsequent resurrection of Triumph may well have had some subliminal influence on my own decision to save Britain from ending up like an empty warehouse with a parliament full of Mr Brown Coats fronting it, trying to pretend everything was all right.

The fact is that we are demonstrably the most innovative race on earth with more significant patents than any other country in the world. Not only this but we also have among the highest levels of technical skill on the planet. You only have to consider the fact that we are the technical base for Formula One and that most constructors' teams are based here (including historically, even Ferrari) as well as those of some of the top racing teams in other international motorsport. For instance, Penske, the most successful Indy car team in American motor racing history are based here, in Poole and Reading.

Our inventive achievements as a nation are legendary. We invented the first proper electronic computer in order to break the German Enigma code in World War II, and then we allowed IBM to beat us into turning it into a commercial product.

We even invented the jet engine in the 1930s, but its inventor Sir Frank Whittle could not persuade the RAF or the British Government to back him.

The jet engine is a perfect example of the sad fact that while British innovators can produce the most important inventions, they are seldom given the backing they need. Just imagine how different the world would be today if the doddering old fools in the RAF high command had backed Whittle in 1930. It would have given us nine whole years to produce an air force of jet-propelled warplanes before the war broke out in 1939.

Think about it: nine years is the equivalent of a century in technological-development terms. We would have had time not only to build an entire fighter command of jet fighters but also an entire bomber command of jet-propelled bombers.

When war broke out in 1939, a British jet-bomber crew could have put the kettle on in Biggin Hill, popped over to Berlin to flatten Hitler's brand-new Reich Chancellery just as its paint was drying, and be back to base before the tea finished brewing.

The irony is that jet engines are actually cheaper to build than conventional piston engines once they are mass produced. Not only that but they run on kerosene – basically domestic heating oil – which costs a fraction of the aero-fuel necessary for piston-engine aircraft.

After the war, Whittle became friends with Hans Von Ohain, who led the German jet-engine development team during the war. This is what he told Whittle: 'If you had been given the money, you would have been six years ahead of us; If Hitler or Goering had heard that there is a man in England who flies in a small experimental plane at 500 m.p.h. and that it is coming into development, it is likely that World War II would not have come into being.'

The far-reaching implications of ignoring even a single significant invention like the jet engine can be catastrophic. Had our top brass not been so short-sighted, millions of lives on all sides could have been saved. Indeed America could have stayed out of the war and Russia would not have been forced into it.

Adopting one man's invention in 1930 would have saved the best part of 450,000 British lives, 420,000 American lives and 26 million Russian lives, 15 million of which were non-combatant civilians. Ultimately, as it would have ended the war before it really even got started, it would also have saved at least 8 million German lives and several hundred-thousand Italian lives.

As the only country in the world with jet fighters and bombers, we could have turned Germany into the biggest lager brewery in the British Empire in less than a month and put Hitler's house-painting skills to good use by making him clean the pigeon crap off Nelson's Column for the rest of his life.

Crucially we would have also retained our position as the world's greatest superpower. It is a sobering thought to consider that failing to adopt the jet engine cost us the British Empire, which was broken up due to the long, protracted and expensive war. I realise that contemporary wisdom would consider that a good thing, but just between you and me, was it really? Let's examine the other side of the coin.

While there is a moral argument that no single country should rule a significant proportion of the globe, if anyone is going to do it, it is certain that only the British are qualified. Our natural sense of diplomacy, fair-mindedness and common sense is unique. I would argue that wherever we went we did more good in the long term than harm.

All empires throughout history have left the conquered with long-term benefits. Take the Romans, for example; they left us, along with all the other countries in their empire, with an amazing road infrastructure and an understanding of sanitation and drainage that was way ahead of its time. In turn the British Empire left India with an extensive railway network and a highly efficient national and local administration blueprint. In the case of both countries these important cultural contributions are still very much in use today.

Would we really be better off if the Romans had not conquered us or would India really be better off if we hadn't run it for a while? All PC nonsense aside, no way! In both cases the countries were given a massive fast-forward butt-kicking into a more advanced state of civilised development.

Plus, come on, please! We must have been doing something right, I mean our empire covered 25 per cent of the globe and 500 million people lived in it – one-fifth of the world's population. At one point we were responsible for 30 per cent of the entire world's output. For a tiny island off the coast of Europe it was one hell of an achievement, unparalleled in the history of the world, and we established the vast majority of it not by force but rather by diplomacy and innovation.

Whichever side of the fence you sit on concerning the British Empire, one fact is beyond dispute: by losing our empire we allowed the USA, which in the pre-war period was just a backward, insular society with a self-sufficient economy and no more influence on world events than somewhere like Australia, to transform itself into the most powerful nation on earth, and just look at the problems that has caused.

When we ran the world, even our enemies respected us for our fair-minded and light-handed approach. As I have said, the British Empire was largely based on trade rather than force, which we resorted to only as the last option, but even when we did, the native survivors of the odd machine-gun massacre would sit around and drink tea with us, mainly because they were so fascinated by our pretty red uniforms and bearskin hats, and in particular because we were still wearing them despite the fact it was 105 degrees in the shade.

Ultimately most countries we controlled ended up copying our way of doing things because they appreciated the fact that we just had so much style and good sense. In contrast, sadly, the Americans have managed to upset every single culture they have come in contact with.

This is mainly because, due to their restricted education system, they have a very insular and an introspective view on life and so they lack our highly developed sense of diplomacy and tact. Furthermore, they have never learnt to appreciate the tactical advantages of going to war wearing interesting hats.

Allowing the Americans to take over our job of ruling the world was like allowing your clumsy younger brother to play with your painstakingly constructed Scalextric set, it could only ever end in disaster. Simply adopting the jet engine in 1930 would have prevented it from happening in the first place, and the world would be a much more peaceful place today.

It is highly unlikely that Al-Qaeda or Isis or any of these other extremist terrorist groups would ever have come into being had the British remained in charge, because the British and the Arabs shared a mutual respect for each other's cultures. For instance, the Arabs worshiped T. E. Lawrence like a living god in World War I because he was the only man in their history who had managed to bring the many disparate and warring nomadic Arabic tribes together to fight and defeat a common enemy, in this case the Turks.

The British could do no wrong in Arabic eyes after that because it was obvious to them that we had made a considerable effort to understand their culture and show them some respect by sending a brilliant military strategist to lead them, one who could speak every dialect of Arabic fluently and who had studied their way of life and history in great detail. They appreciated that he was also a brave warrior so dedicated to his duty that he was not only prepared to die fighting beside them but also to go to any lengths to fit in even if this meant going to war riding a camel and wearing a long white dress.

Look, please do not misunderstand me, I am not seriously suggesting that the British Empire should be intact today for a single second, but what I am thinking is that had World War II not forced it to be so rapidly – perhaps a better word is *instantly* dismantled and replaced by American foreign policy, which to put it mildly can only be described as insensitive at best, then there is a good chance that our steadying presence would have gently maintained stability in the world for much longer.

Then, in a much less pressurised scenario, the British Empire could have been organically phased out over the natural course of several decades due to the natural desire for self-determination among the populations of its colonies, each of which could have parted on friendly terms from British control when they were ready to stand alone.

Anyone who thinks that last statement is patronising should take a long hard, and dare I say it, perhaps for the first time in their lives, *objective* look at the state of those former colonies today, and should they find it possible to override the prejudice ingrained by a PCB anti–British Empire, brainwashing education, ask themselves in all honestly whether the general populations of these countries are really better off today or not as a result of swapping one overlord for another.

Yes indeed, ignoring our inventive spirit has had devastating long-term consequences.

The fact is that from penicillin in 1928 to the World Wide Web in 1989, the actual Internet itself, upon which the world relies daily, we have invented just about everything that has ever mattered to mankind, and yet time and time again since the early to mid-twentieth century we have stood aside and let other countries not only exploit the idea but also take false credit for it.

The really sad part is that we have now and have always had the innovative and the technical ability. In that amazing era of the Industrial Revolution of the late nineteenth century we also had the confidence to back all of our great innovators like Isambard Kingdom Brunel for instance, which is why we led the world in technology and engineering from early Victorian times right through the turn of the twentieth century into the Edwardian period.

However, strangely for such an otherwise self-confident culture, it seems that ever since the Great Depression of 1929 to 1939 the key ingredient we have lacked is the faith to invest in our own abilities, I am not sure why this has come about but it is very unjustified and living proof of that is John Bloor who has heroically and ably proved with the successful rebirth of Triumph Motorcycles that we can be just as good as we have ever been in the past, if we just start believing in ourselves again.

Time for a change of attitude, then.

Corporation tax and bank contribution

In my view it is essential to encourage entrepreneurship in this country. When I left the armed services I went into business as a manufacturer and I know just how hard it is to get a business going and to find finance.

Well I decided to do something to change this lamentable

situation, so now 2 per cent of all corporation tax is allocated for a central business investment fund to help entrepreneurs to get new businesses off the ground. A change in the law also now makes it compulsory for all banks to match this funding pound for pound at an interest rate fixed at 4 per cent over base rate. To spread this risk for the banks, they pay into a central fund and receive back a proportion of the net interest revenue, which is linked to the proportion of investment made by them.

Even if 50 per cent of the start-ups fail, the banks are still receiving 2 per cent over base without any administration costs, which is the equivalent of at least another per cent in comparison to a normal business loan.

From the perspective of the new businesses, as 50 percent of the investment contribution is an interest-free grant from the government's side, the overall investment package helps businesses get off the ground for the equivalent of 2 per cent over base rate. How much this investment package comprises depends on the requirement of the new business.

A new business development department called the NBDD, which is entirely staffed by ex-entrepreneurs, makes the decision based on a combination of a straightforward points formula and their own experience and discretion. Investments over £250,000 must be signed off by three NBDD directors. The largest single investment to date, including the 50 per cent bank contribution, is £23 million, which was to a company producing cutting-edge software.

A similar scheme also now helps existing businesses, which have been established over two years with proven expansion potential.

The most important aspect of these two schemes is that for the first time in many decades banks actually have to do what they were originally designed to do, which is to lend money to real businesses rather than use the money their customers have on deposit in savings accounts, on which they pay hardly any interest, to provide them with collateral necessary to leverage massive international currency exchange scams like manipulating the LIBOR rate.

Even if as many as 50 per cent of the new start-ups fail, the net benefit to the economy in getting the other 50 per cent, which succeed, off the ground, vastly outweighs this in the long run. Every unemployed person who can be taken off benefits because a new job has been created is not only a financial saving to the nation but also has a positive social impact because they get work experience and a career start. Even the entrepreneurs who fail the first or second time will mostly learn from their mistakes and go on to succeed in the end.

To deter potential fraud, the minimum penalty for setting up a bogus business purely with an intention of taking the grant and bank loan is ten years inside. All businesses in the schemes are allocated an experienced mentor from the NBDD, and part of their job is to ensure that the investment funds are being used correctly. So Mr Brown Coat staring at oil stains on the ceiling while pretending to run an empty warehouse would not pass muster, for instance.

Corporation Tax and Bank Contribution, working well, GTJD.

50/50 Inventor Centre

To prevent future catastrophes like giving away the invention of the computer and the jet engine to other countries who then take the credit, I ordered the construction of three massive new inventor centres to assist inventors in developing their inventions and in retaining the benefit of them for Britain. One centre is based near Reading, a second is based near Manchester and a third at Edinburgh.

This is how they work: the idea is that an inventor can bring their invention to their nearest Inventor Centre and once it has passed an approval process involving a viability analysis by designers and engineers, it is then investigated by intellectual property lawyers to determine if it would infringe any existing patents and also to assess the probability of successfully obtaining its own. If it passes these tests, it is then accepted for the scheme.

At this point the inventor has enjoyed the benefit of a dispassionate and professional due diligence analysis for free, which otherwise would been a very costly exercise.

Now the inventor may, if they wish, enter into a contract with the Inventor Centre in which the centre will, in return for 50 per cent of the future royalties or profits from the invention, fund the cost and provide the expertise to develop the invention into a viable product while at the same time push it through all the necessary legal steps to acquire patents or register design rights for it.

This arrangement not only allows an inventor to get his or her idea turned into a reality very quickly but also at no cost or risk to themselves. The extensive resources at the disposal of Inventor Centres ensure that the whole process is executed to the highest standard, which gives the invention a very much higher chance of commercial success than it would otherwise have.

For every invention that sees the light of day, there are hundreds that do not, simply because the cost of product development and of overcoming the legal hurdles are greater than most people can afford. Not only that, but without the necessary support and expertise, most people do not know where or how to start.

To facilitate the 50/50 arrangement in a practical way, legally, a new company is incorporated for each invention with 50 per cent of the shares being held by the inventor and the remaining 50 per cent held by the Inventor Centre. While the inventor gets full credit for the invention, all IP rights are allocated to this separate legal entity.

Another important benefit for the inventors is that this arrangement also protects them from being ripped off by unscrupulous multi-national companies with regards to royalty payments, which frequently happens. Nobody would risk ripping off a company in which 50 per cent of the shares are held by the Inventor Centre because they would be defrauding an arm of the British government, and at the end of that arm lies a fist called the SMOG.

These Inventor Centres are not just about helping inventors turn dreams into commercial reality, albeit that this is their primary function, but they are also designed to overcome and indeed hopefully to change one of Britain's most fundamental business-related problems that has held us back since the Industrial Revolution of the nineteenth century, namely job snobbery.

For some reason here in Britain people who work in offices shuffling paper, like intellectual property lawyers, regard themselves as a superior race to engineers. This is not so much the lawyers' fault but rather due to the fact that unlike most other civilised countries we look down on anyone who is involved with the practical side of making things. The further away from reality and the more ethereal a person's job is, the higher the regard in which we hold them, whereas the closer their work takes them to the nuts and bolts, the less we think of them.

Even if an engineer holds a doctorate in rocket propulsion and has an IQ of 160, any old IP lawyer with half his brainpower is still regarded as a better potential son-in-law by Mrs Bucket. This utterly illogical job snobbery lies at the heart of Britain's problem. Because the lawyers are too self-important to talk to the designers and engineers, the process of developing inventions is highly inefficient.

Months or even years can be unnecessarily and expensively wasted going down a particular design path that subsequently turns out to infringe existing IP or current patents. Had it been possible to organise more cooperation between lawyers and designers in the early stages this would have ensured the adoption of an alternative and viable design route.

Right, so this is how I solved the problem: I called in my top architects and explained that I wanted them to design a blueprint for the three new Inventor Centres in which offices for IP lawyers were to be situated on ground-floor level around a central hub containing the design studios and workshops of the engineers.

All the offices, whether they be for engineers designers or IP lawyers, were to be constructed of soundproof glass so everyone could feel that they were working right in the heart of the action, with CAD machines grinding, lathes turning and arc welders sparking away in the massive central hub around which they all worked.

This way the IP lawyers would be part of the design process as it happened rather than being part of an aloof profession that is consulted only after an invention has been developed, often from a legal stand point, incorrectly or less efficiently than it needed to be.

Having built the first Inventor Centre, we ensured that it was staffed with the brightest senior designers, engineers and IP lawyers. The latter were picked not only for their expertise but also their willingness to embrace the new concept of becoming part of a new hands-on approach.

The various professions were briefed that they must find a way of working closely together on each and every project. So an IP lawyer attends daily meetings with the designers and engineers and spends as much time in the workshop with them as in his office.

Conversely, the engineers are able to drop in to the lawyer's office at any time to check whether going down a certain design route is a good or bad decision from an IP standpoint. I gambled that this bringing together of cultures would rapidly break down the inherent barriers between the professions and establish mutual respect in that unique way, which as my military service taught me, only comes about when people work closely together to achieve common goals.

Unsurprisingly perhaps, this gamble has paid off. Within a matter of weeks, IP lawyers in the first Inventor Centre were learning to look at things from an engineer's perspective, and just as importantly designers and engineers were learning, if not exactly to think like lawyers, then at least to consider the legal implications of design aspects at every turn.

The efficiency gained through this breaking down of established professional barriers is inestimable. Britain will now churn out successfully patented designs at an unprecedented rate to the great benefit of our economy and our status on the world stage.

One sunny spring morning I slipped surreptitiously out of 10 Downing Street and made an unannounced visit to the first Inventor Centre near Reading, about three months after it was opened. I arrived at about 10 a.m., and was delighted to see that none of the IP lawyers were in their offices but were instead to be found with their shirtsleeves rolled up working right beside the engineers in the workshop and looking like they had never enjoyed themselves so much in their lives. When I saw that, I knew for certain then that we had achieved the objective.

Of course, it being a lovely spring day, I had to make the journey there and back on my new Triumph Tiger 800, which runs like a Swiss watch and doesn't leak oil. On the way back I couldn't help myself from thinking just how much trouble I could have got into if they had been as good as this when I was seventeen. Then again, perhaps it is a good thing they weren't, because my staff at No. 10 would probably be dealing with several dozen paternity suits about now.

Inventor Centre, what a cracking idea Gromit! GTJD.

Chapter five

Law and Order Part I

There were two major areas I knew I had to address in the important area of law and order. First of all, 64 per cent of criminals were reoffending when they got out of custody and mostly went on to commit more serious crimes than the ones they had been incarcerated for in the first place, so all the current prison system represented was a university for criminality. The second problem was that punishment had become so lenient that it was no longer a deterrent. A radical shake-up was clearly required.

In the last few decades the criminal population of Britain multiplied dramatically. In my view the most significant causes of this were the removal of traditional discipline methods in schools, and the progressive march of ever more lenient sentencing, to the point where any deterrent value had all but disappeared.

I firmly believe that both of these elements were entirely due to the sinister and underhand influence of the PCB, who over the decades have infiltrated every single nook and cranny of our culture in the successful pursuit of their own empowerment.

Crime had become a massively expensive drain on Britain's economy. I had always suspected that the real cost of keeping a criminal in prison was many times higher than the £40,000 per annum that was admitted to by the government departments. When I came to power and had access to the full information, my hunch proved correct.

Sure enough, it turned out that successive governments had been able to hide such massive money drains as building upkeep, maintenance and the cost of the parole and other criminal support services in budgets other than those associated directly with prisoner upkeep. I had my whizz kids do a forensic analysis of the true costs and it turned out that when everything was taken into account, the real cost was over £100,000 a year per prisoner. At that rate it would be cheaper to the taxpayer to put them up at the Ritz.

Once this true calculation was then multiplied by the prison population, it became evident that the total figure represented an annual drain on Britain's economy of over £87.6 billion, which is utterly ludicrous and quite unacceptable. It is the same cost as running the entire NHS.

I quickly realised that no matter how drastic and cold-bloodied it sounds, there was only one way of sorting the matter out. They all had to go.

After all, what is the point of allowing criminals to exist in our society? When they are in jail they cost a fortune, and when they are out they cost even more. They are not just totally unproductive but counterproductive. Why should we spend £100,000 a year keeping a totally selfish negative individual in prison when millions of people who have worked all their lives, paid tax and contributed to society, cannot get proper health care when they need it and die before their time?

With an ever-increasing burden growing on an already overstretched health service, the choice is stark; you can either allow 20,000–30,000 decent hard-working productive people to die unnecessarily every year due to a lack of appropriate health care, year after year for evermore, creating a death toll in the tens of millions eventually, or you can simply get rid of 87,600-odd totally unproductive, evil, selfish people once and for all, and then, by introducing sentencing with an effective deterrent value, make sure that they are not replaced.

In my view, when faced with balancing the lives, health and happiness of millions of good productive people against the deaths of a few thousand useless criminals, the matter becomes no longer a choice, but a duty.

Politicians have limited options on a matter like this, but there is no point in being a dictator unless you take the plunge and, while suspending all normal morality, just do the right thing, no matter how horrific and distasteful it may seem.

After all, democratically elected prime ministers make supposedly legitimate decisions in the name of Britain to go to war, sometimes based on very dubious grounds and on the thinnest of pretexts, and in doing so kill tens of thousands of innocent non-combatant civilians in other countries. So what's the difference morally? Especially as the voting public are quite happy to support this example of mass murder by re-electing the same people again and again without a second thought.

So this was my plan.

One, it was transparently obvious that the entire prison population, including psychopathic serial killers incarcerated in secure mental hospitals, who are especially expensive to keep, had to be disposed of quickly and simultaneously. And, as if that wasn't a challenge enough, for the sake of Britain's worldwide reputation it also had to look like an accident.

Two, it was imperative to prevent new criminals from starting out on a career in crime in the first place, by introducing a much tougher and more straightforward sentencing system, which would create a really effective deterrent.

Double Up

While I was thinking how to achieve the first, I got on with addressing the second. I decided to create a new sentencing system, which was considerably harsher than the existing one but also easy to understand and fair. I called it Double Up.

It works like this: crimes are categorised in order of seriousness from 1 to 30, with level 1 representing minor crimes like petty theft and shoplifting right through to level 30 representing the most serious for violent crimes like armed robbery, murder, mugging, aggravated rape and aggravated burglary.

The punishment for these crimes were mandatory sentences for which every day would be served with no parole available, particularly as I scrapped the entire parole service as in my view it represented an unnecessary overhead.

In order to allow a new criminal the chance to turn their life around, Double Up starts with relatively short sentences for minor crimes, which double up with every repeat offence of the same level or increase according to the level of crime. For instance, let's say a teenager decides to joyride a car, that offence is now regarded as car theft and is a level 2 crime as is any vehicle theft, for which the first offence is two years in jail or in a young offenders' institution if under eighteen. In either institution, it is now mandatory to serve the full term.

After this criminal is released, should he or she then decide to commit a level 2 crime again, whether this is car theft or another level 2 crime such as vandalising a bus, he or she receives four years. If they are so mind-boggling stupid as to continue such behaviour, it progresses to eight years, sixteen years, thirty-two years, sixty-four years and so on.

However, should the same criminal reoffend on a second occasion by committing a higher level of crime such as a level 3 crime like burglary, for which the first offence carries a three-year sentence, he or she will now serve six years, as it is their second offence and the higher level crime sets the term.

If the next offence is a lower level 1 offence like shoplifting, the lower-level crime sets the term but again the term is doubled, as it is the second offence, so in this case it would be two years.

I firmly believe that if a criminal knows precisely what his sentence will be if he gets caught, then this is a much greater deterrent to reoffending.

It was important to make this system simple enough not only for the most moronic glue-sniffing scumbag to understand, but also for the geriatric judiciary, many of whom are totally senile. So to keep it simple, the level of crime represents the first offence jail time, for instance level 3 equals three years for the first offence. As these terms are mandatory with no discretion to worry about, the whole criminal justice system is now massively streamlined and infinitely more cost effective.

However, the priority of Double Up was to discourage crime rather than just deal with offenders after they had committed crime.

After all, keeping any criminals is an expense to be avoided, and while, with a bit of luck, I might get away with disposing of the entire prison population once, clearly I couldn't keep doing it or it would affect Britain's reputation in the eyes of the world as a civilised and just country.

In order to maximise the deterrent effect of Double Up and also to give those criminals still abroad in society the best chance to change their ways, I decided to use the two most powerful mediums available to me to advertise the new system for three months before it came into effect – TV and social media. The most logical time to start the campaign was the quarter running up to a new year so that there could be no misunderstanding as to when it came into effect.

So for the three months leading up to the first New Year's Day of my term, the public were bombarded by a highly creative advertising campaign twenty-four hours a day, on TV, radio and all social media platforms. The objective was to illustrate how the system worked and to emphasise that it would start on New Year's Day. The carefully crafted TV adverts featured chilling images of prison life and always ended with a heavy prison door slamming shut with a distinctive clang.

By law, every second commercial break contained these adverts and it was impossible to escape their depressing message. Very soon even I got fed up with them and wondered if I really had needed to insist on three months of the bloody things, but it was too late to change that.

Photoshopped images of various young men or women turning old in prison, decade by decade, were featured both on a massive nationwide poster campaign and also in endless inescapable pop-up ads on the web.

Every ex-con whose address was known to the authorities was sent a personalised letter containing a section in red ink outlining exactly how this new system would affect him or her if they offended again. For instance if an ex-con had already being jailed three times for burglary, irrespective of the ludicrously lenient sentences he had received previously, which had obviously done nothing to deter him from reoffending, this time he would receive 4 x 3 years, equalling twelve years with no parole.

The police were encouraged, whenever practical, to visit ex-cons in their area with letters like this and to make them sign a copy as proof that they had the new system explained to them.

One way or another about 85 per cent of ex-cons were success-fully contacted.

Sure enough, all this effort was rewarded. Once the New Year started both petty and professional criminal activity dropped 98 per cent and has stayed that way ever since. Police stations and remand centres stood eerily empty throughout the land. Most days you can hear a pin drop in the main court of the Old Bailey and the other criminal courtrooms.

Within a year, 87 per cent of criminal barristers had left the bar and gone abroad to seek employment. They weren't missed.

Apart from the occasional crime of passion, general crime for all intents and purposes has now simply ceased to exist in Britain.

Double Up, good plan then, certainly GTJD.

Drugs trade

Drugs are one of Britain's biggest problems and this is how I tackled it. First of all, dealing drugs in any quantity at all, even a personal-use quantity to a friend, became a level 15 crime, making even a first offence a guaranteed fifteen years. As the majority of dealers had at least one other conviction, for most this would mean thirty years. This alone cut drug distribution by more than 90 per cent when Double Up came into force.

However, drug dealers are often clever and highly motivated people who find ways of operating behind desperate junkies, so this alone was not going to Get The Job Done.

So this is what I did: firstly, I brought the finest chemists in academia together into a think tank headed up by a Cambridge professor who once lectured me in the subject. I ordered them to produce a very effective but harmless synthetic cocaine substitute, which was packaged and licensed to be sold in certain types of bars, normally cocktail bars rather than ordinary pubs. It would be sold subject to even more strict regulations than alcohol at slightly less than the average cost of illegal street cocaine.

Once produced, we branded it Charlie, and I decided that all profits would be distributed among existing programmes for drug rehabilitation.

Charlie

Once on the market, largely thanks to its consistent nature, Charlie users soon felt it gave a better high than the multiply cut and unreliable street cocaine they were used to. They also appreciated the advantage of knowing that unlike conventional coke, it had no serious long-term health or mental-health implications, such as psychosis, and that it contained only pure ingredients.

The product also has a unique detectable chemical trace. This allows traffic police to measure a driver's consumption of it just like alcohol. Users are reminded of this fact on the packaging, along with guidelines to safe use, particularly when mixed with alcohol.

The only other legal obtainable drug is medical marijuana, supplied free on the NHS through bona-fide doctor's prescription for the likes of arthritis suffers. At least this has put an end to pensioners growing their own under lamps in the attic and then, due to the unnaturally high levels of tetra-hydro-cannabinol, known as THC, in the genetically modified skunk this produced, getting themselves embarrassingly arrested for pushing each other down the high street in supermarket trolley races.

Once the illegal consumption of unlicensed cocaine or any other drug became a level 2 crime, no one was prepared to risk two years inside to consume a product inferior to one they could legally buy in most bars. This, in addition to the harsh fifteen-year minimum sentences for drug dealing in even the smallest volume put a swift end to the illegal drug trade.

Gangs

I hate gang culture on any level and made its destruction a top priority. In one forty-eight-hour period, the leadership of all major gangs (MG) and organised crime (OC) in the UK were rounded up by my new elite unit called Special Military Operations Group, or

SMOG. This unit is comprised of highly trained and very heavily armed serving and ex-Special Forces volunteers from elite regiment members such as the SAS, SBS, Pathfinders, Paras and the Royal Marines.

This crack new unit had a wide remit as to how they arrested the targets and then extracted such information as was necessary to ensure the complete destruction of that particular gang or organised crime structure and the recovery of as much illegally obtained money and assets as possible. I called the operation Gang Busters.

One of the keys to success was that the entire operation was in the hands of the intelligence services and the military. Knowing that, sadly, the police are riddled with informants, I decided to keep them completely in the dark. Whenever the police saw the SMOG in action, wearing black combat kit and displaying police logos on their black flack jackets and helmets, they assumed that they were from one of their own specialist armed response units and so were not alerted to the real situation.

Gang Busters

Gang Busters was the single largest crime busting operation the UK had ever seen. It went largely unreported in the media except where unavoidable, in which case a suitable cover story was reported to the public, blaming anti-terrorism. GCHQ, the electronic intelligence and warfare centre in Cheltenham, made sure that senior crime figures could not communicate with each other by landline or mobile for the forty-eight-hours it took to snatch all the targeted individuals.

The OC figures who regarded themselves as too well connected to ever be arrested were the first to have their front doors blown off their hinges in the early hours of the morning. In some cases they were taken from locations abroad and sometimes even from their yachts. This was always executed with the extreme speed, efficiency and overwhelming force that only the best special forces in the world can deliver.

All of them, under interrogation, expressed amazement that their usual police informants, some of whom were senior officers, had not tipped them off in advance.

Thanks to the cooperation of MI5, MI6 and GCHQ, not a single UK senior crime figure escaped arrest by the SMOG anywhere on the planet.

To prevent the top men being replaced by their lieutenants, every one of these potential candidates was identified and snatched within the same forty-eight-hour period and sent to the interrogation centre.

Lower-level individuals who might possibly posses some management potential were also detained while the SMOG determined if any of them were significant or not, from their interrogation of the senior crime figures.

Any employees at the bottom of the food chain, such as armed bodyguards, proved to be no match for heavily armed Special Forces operatives of SMOG, who shot dead anyone with a firearm on sight on my direct orders. Where this occurred abroad, the bodies were repatriated to the UK in body bags, to ensure no evidence was left for the nosy local police to concern themselves with.

The SMOG operatives were not only paid well in terms of basic salary but also enjoyed a very generous commission structure in order to motivate them to recover as much money as possible from senior MG and OC figures.

For every pound they extracted, the individual eight-man team received 25 per cent tax free, with the overall Gang Busters programme receiving a further 25 per cent. The remaining 50 per cent was allocated to helping rehabilitate the victims of crime, particularly human-trafficking and sex-slave victims. To learn how some of this was put to good use, I refer you to the later chapter on education.

The OC and MG busts led to the recovery of many billions in cash funds and assets. Many of the SMOG had become tax-free multi-millionaires by the time operation Gang Busters was over. The fact that the operatives had a vested interest in keeping the gang lords alive made sure that the interrogation methods, while undoubtedly very robust, did not go too far as to cause death. Justice still had to be seen to be done.

On the subject of justice, by the time they left the custody of the SMOG to be sent for trial, every one of the senior OC figures and MG leaders had proved exceptionally cooperative in 'voluntarily' confessing to a staggering amount of serious crime. In fact they had provided so much damning evidence against themselves that the average multiplication of level 30 sentencing was six hundred years in custody.

Little did they know they wouldn't have to serve even a single year; they were off to Davy Jones's locker where they belonged.

Chapter six

Law and Order Part II

The prison ship cruise

The problem was how to dispose of 87,653 criminals simultane-ously and get away with it. The answer came one morning in a flash of inspiration while reviewing the plans for the new Royal Yacht; I would send the whole lot on a nice little Atlantic cruise.

I announced to the media that as a cost-saving measure we would follow the example of Norway, who send their prisoners to Denmark, by subcontracting the whole ludicrously expensive business of keeping criminals in prison to another country.

Once word got out, we received surprisingly strong tenders from all corners of the globe, some of them potentially acceptable, from places like India and Australia, right across the board to rather more colourful options, including a proposal from the population of Papua New Guinea, who wanted to eat them and sell their shrunken heads as tourist souvenirs. However, amusing as all this was, I needed a plausible solution that would appear acceptable to the rest of the world for the sake of Britain's reputation.

I was hoping the Americans would be interested, but even the £30,000 per prisoner I offered could not tempt them. However, when the news reached the Cuban government, they jumped at the chance. As a delegation of high-ranking officials from the Cuban Ministry of the Interior enthusiastically pointed out to me in 10 Downing Street, Cuba, being over twice the size of the UK but with a sixth of the population, could easily accommodate the prisoners in a humane environment with a mild and stable climate. It could also provide an exceptionally healthy diet for them consisting of totally natural home-produced food.

They were equally keen to point out that as one in seven of the population is a doctor, the prisoners would receive very high standard of medical care. They refrained from saying far better, in fact, than they would get at home, but I knew that's what they were quite understandably thinking. *Not for long, my old cocks*, I thought. *That's what this is all about. If you only knew the truth.*

They emphasised that Cuba was a highly secure island with a very well-equipped army, navy, coastguard, and air force, and not having EU law to worry about, they assured me that any attempt by rescuers to spring convicts from the well-guarded jails would be met with the ultimate in state-of-the-art deadly force.

I wasn't that surprised the Cubans were keen to pitch for the contract, with the average wage for a professional such as a architect, university lecturer or brain surgeon being fixed at the sterling equivalent of about £50 per month in Cuba, the opportunity of receiving £30,000 per annum a head in a real, hard international currency was almost more than the Cuban elite could ever have dreamt of, and they bent over backwards to meet every one of the stringent assurances that I made a play of seeking from them.

I suggested to them that as Cuba had a lot of surplus agricultural land, the low-security prisoners from the likes of Ford open prison, where Conservative MPs and wayward members of the British aristocracy often end up, could run prison farms and produce enough food for the entire prison population. They loved the idea. I could tell they were warming to me; they even asked if I would like to pop over and take a tour of Cuba to see if I had any other practical suggestions about the place.

Now I had made their Christmas card list, I pushed home the advantage. For the sake of Britain's reputation, I needed to appear to be sending her prisoners to the best possible service provider, and the better the cover story looked the easier it would be to achieve my real objective of getting rid of the lot of them permanently.

So while the Cubans were all wound up about the whole idea, I put it to them that if they built really spacious new jails with large open-air exercise yards and so forth, there would be a fantastic PR opportunity to let the world's media compare their ultra-humane treatment of prisoners with what the Americans had been doing in Guantanamo Bay. Which after all, they could remind the world, is Cuban territory occupied against Cuba's will by the Yanks. How good for Cuba's reputation in the eyes of the world would that be?

I pointed out that the very fact Britain had chosen Cuba over all other international tenders, to entrust its prison population with would be considered the highest possible endorsement in the eyes of the rest of the world, because everyone respects Britain's humanitarian ethic.

Well I can tell you, by the time I had finished that pitch, they were literally choking on their Monte Christos with excitement. I had definitely become their new best dictator and they assured me no effort would be spared in creating the most civilised, clean and spacious jails in the world.

They even offered to build new mini airports right next to each of the new state-of-the-art jails, which they assured me, incidentally, that they could construct in less than a year. Furthermore, they even offered to fly the prisoners' relatives in and out of Cuba for free for visiting days, which they said could be achieved by picking them up from regional airports all around Britain.

Well you can afford to do that sort of thing if the Chinese have given you your planes for free and you are paying your pilots £50 a month and your aircrew a tenner apiece, can't you?

My PR machine was now working overtime to sell the public the radical concept that we could cut our prison costs by 70 per cent by subcontracting the incarceration of prisoners to Cuba. I promised that free shuttle services to the airports would be provided for prisoners' relatives, most of whom were quite enthusiastic about the chance of some free sunshine, especially after Cuba had produced glitzy video presentations of the proposed new jails, depicting bright comfortably appointed reception rooms for visitors that were in stark contrast to their depressing experience of visiting prisons here.

The most resistance came from people who thought that the prisoners were going to be treated too well, with prison farms to play in and so forth. The tabloid press displayed Cuban PR pictures of the proposed jails, which made them look more like holiday camps than penal institutions.

One newspaper made it a front-page article, carrying a computer-generated picture of a luxurious-looking Cuban jail cell under the headline Camp Cuba, under which it listed all the amenities available to prisoners including football pitches.

I countered all this flak by stating that Britain could only entertain such a move if it could be sure that its prisoners would receive the highest standard of care. However, I was secretly pleased at their reaction as they were playing into my hands. I instructed the press department to exaggerate any criticism I was receiving from the public. I needed to be above suspicion when I made my move.

After all, how could a man with a reputation for being far too soft and considerate to prisoners, possibly be suspected of conspiring to drown the lot deliberately?

I had no intention of wasting £30,000 a head per annum on a single one of them. More importantly, in order to ensure the creation of a new crime-free Britain, I did not want them coming back and continuing their criminal careers once they returned from their Cuban holiday camp.

In particular, now that all the top gang lords and drug lords were going to be on the cruise, I was determined to ensure that they could never use their criminal connections to influence criminal activities in Britain again, even from their cells in Cuba.

There was another reason I was happy for the press to criticise the swish new Cuban jails and exaggerate the benefits and facilities available to the UK prisoners going to them. I knew that our prison population read the same newspapers, and it suited me very well if they all thought they were going to a much more pleasant environment and going to get some sunshine.

I also suspected that some of the long-term prisoners would incorrectly believe that escape from Cuba would be a real possibility. This all helped to ensure that we were not going to encounter any problems from the inmates during the transportation process.

When dealing with such a large body of people, an enthusiastic attitude and a high state of morale among the group are both very helpful.

My main problem now was how to get the entire prison population together on the high seas at once. The pressure was on. I had only twelve months, while the Cubans built their new jails, to work out a practical plan to dispose of the prison population. I vaguely thought about a flotilla of prison ships chained together, which might just plausibly pull each other down in a bad storm, but that just did not scan. However, one of my researchers found the perfect solution.

In 2009 the largest passenger vessel in the world, named *Oasis of the Seas*, set sail. This monstrous ship weighing in at over 226,000 tonnes was designed to carry 6,000 passengers on its sixteen decks, in unprecedented luxury. It had cabins larger than many normal houses, at 1,600 square feet, promenades full of shops, swimming pools galore, gyms, several bars and night clubs and even its own version of New York's Central Park, with 12,000 plants and fifty-eight mature trees. This mega ship was designed to set a new standard in cruise ships.

After the launch of this industry changing mega-cruiser, a few more ships of similar design followed, each slightly larger than the last. All proved to be great commercial successes thanks to demand from the world's wealthy retired population, who purchased permanent cabin space in order to spend the remainder of their lives floating around the world playing golf and sunbathing in tax-free luxury.

Any guilt they might have felt about enjoying such an extravagant retirement was alleviated once they discovered that if they were buried at sea and their death recorded in international waters, then, as the ships were registered in Panama, providing they invested their cash offshore, their heirs could get away with avoiding inheritance taxes.

These new mega-cruiser retirement homes proved so financially successful that, as one might expect in the highly competive world of shipbuilding, it was only a matter of time before the Chinese decided to produce a ship more than double the size of *Oasis of the*

Sea at 524,000 tonnes. Actually they decided to build two.

I found out that the first one of these monstrous ships, called MS *The Universe*, had just completed her first sea trials as a stripped-out, bare vessel with its first-fit completed, including cabins with working electrical and plumbing services, but no decoration or luxuries yet – perfect for my intended use.

The Universe had been designed to carry 15,000 people in absolute luxury on thirty-three decks. It could, with minimum temporary adaptation, easily accommodate the 87,653 prisoners in basic but by no means inhumane conditions. It would represent a cabin sleeping-space ratio of less than six to one, which in bunk beds would be perfectly acceptable.

The American and Canadian soldiers crossing the Atlantic in troopships in World War II slept in far more cramped conditions than that. They slept in bunks twenty layers high (in fact, in 1942, *The Queen Mary* at just over 82,000-tonnes carried between 15,000 and 16,000-troops per Atlantic crossing). However, in contrast, in this mega-cruiser, some of the cabins were as large as 3,000 square feet and so were quite spacious enough to accommodate a hundred or so prisoners sleeping in standard jail-issue double-height bunks, with no less personal space each than in an average British prison.

I justified the decision to transport the prisoners in one vessel to the media on the grounds that it was more secure and logistically easier for the Navy to guard. With my PR machine going flat out to ensure that an astonished public were kept mesmerised by the mind-blowing statistics of the massive vessel, no one argued.

At first the owners of *The Universe* were not keen to lease the ship for such a purpose, but when they were offered £100 million for the five-week voyage they saw things differently. It was agreed that they would be paid a £10-million deposit within a week of sailing and the balance upon safe arrival at Cuba.

The innocent and the useful

Before we emptied the jails, I had my researchers check through the prison population to see if there was anyone who should be given the benefit of the doubt or was worth saving.

I instructed them to select anyone in the retrial pipeline for extraction providing they had never offended before. If they had a criminal record, as far as I was concerned, whether they were innocent or not of their current conviction, they were still criminals and they were going on the cruise.

The other instruction I gave my team was to look for any really bright people with special skills or qualifications who might be able to serve their country better by helping my various programmes.

The Oxford professor I used for the immigration programme was picked out in this way for his expertise in EU law, along with a couple of other really bright people whom I could see being useful at some point. Both of them, like the absent-minded professor, were also serving sentences for crimes of passion and therefore not strictly criminals.

The Universe was to be crewed by well-armed SMOG personnel, all originally from the Special Boat Service, or SBS, the elite Special Forces regiment that I served in myself. In addition, *The Universe* was to be escorted by a fully armed Royal Naval carrier group consisting of two Type 45 destroyers, two Type 23 frigates, one Wave-class fast fleet tanker and two Wave-class fast fleet supply ships – due to the amount of food required for such a large number of prisoners – an aircraft carrier and one Astute-class nuclear attack submarine, so it was not necessary to be concerned too much about the prisoners on board attempting escape.

The female prisoners were billeted on a separate deck to the male convicts, and as a precaution the dangerous inmates from secure mental institutions like Broadmoor were isolated from the rest of the inmates. Better to keep all the nutters in one area, it was agreed. So we put them in the massive central recreation area, which had already been planted with several hundred mature trees in preparation for the development of a large park. It even had an electronically controlled freshwater river flowing through it, and most of it was already covered by neatly laid green turf.

Perhaps on reflection this was an unwise place to put those who were already insane. The improbable experience of finding themselves in a beautiful, cultivated park while being incarcerated in the bowels of a gigantic ship was too much for many of them to deal with after decades of being locked up in solitary confinement.

Many of the strait-jacketed mental cases, all of whom were drugged up to the eyeballs to keep them sedated, roamed around the artificial grounds in a considerable state of confusion, often staring for hours at notices politely requesting them not to ride bicycles on the grass and to place dog poo in the appropriate receptacles.

To ensure total security on the voyage, there was a two-mile floating-security exclusion zone around the flotilla, with a five-mile no-fly zone enforced by two fully armed jet fighters on permanently rotating twenty-four-hour guard duty backed up by forty-six other fighters on the carrier and a squadron of armed Apache attack helicopters.

So tight was security that the press was warned that any aircraft or vessel attempting to enter the exclusion zone would be fired upon without warning and destroyed.

However, far out to sea one vessel was shadowing the convoy. It was a massive container ship that was under the control of a skeleton crew consisting of another SMOG unit, once again, all ex-SBS men. Six weeks or so earlier, while disguised as pirates, with all of them wearing appropriate tribal clothing with shemaghs wrapped around faces darkened by a special black waterproof camouflage oil designed for night-time operations at sea, and led by two officers speaking fluent Somali to lend authenticity, they had snatched the vessel off the coast of Somalia in the dead of night.

Having let the twenty-seven-man crew escape to safety in the ship's spacious and fully enclosed twenty-nine-foot lifeboat in the early hours of the following morning, and having first ensured that it was generously stocked with food and fresh water, they had sailed the massive ship around the Horn of Africa. From then on, while keeping well clear of the West African shipping lanes, they had made their way out into the Atlantic to intercept the convoy.

Because *The Universe* was the biggest vessel on the planet, I needed a very large ship to sink her with. I was quite confident that the explosive charges my men had concealed in the keel of the gigantic cruise ship would ensure a swift result. However, from a media perspective, it was essential that if an accidental collision with another ship was to appear to be the cause of the disaster, it had to be a sufficiently catastrophic one to provide a plausible explanation of why she sank with no survivors.

Once again my research team had come up with a suitable candidate, it was one of the largest cargo ships in the world.

In November 2012 a new class of container ship took to the seas, at over 150,000 tonnes loaded, this 1,300 foot monster, named *Marco Polo* as it was the first of the Explorer class, dwarfed all other container ships afloat. However, like the new mega-cruise ships, it was only a matter of time before it was itself outclassed. Only eight months later, in July 2013, the Maersk Triple E-class container ship, the *MC-Kinney Miller,* went into service at 1,312 foot and 165,000 tonnes.

The race had begun. Every few months a larger ship was built until it culminated in a class of 210,000 tonne 1,654-foot behemoths know as the Titan class, named not after famous explorers this time but the Greek gods of the sea. It was one of these, *Phorcys,* appropriately named after the god of the hidden dangers of the deep, which was now waiting to intercept the convoy.

Two and a half days after leaving Southampton, *The Universe,* carrying the entire 87,653 prison population, was sailing in deep water well over the European Continental Shelf and therefore beyond any possible future salvage, it was now just a matter of deciding on an appropriate night to stage the collision.

The first two nights in deep ocean were clear and there was good visibility from the starlit night sky above. However, on the third night a dense fog bank had formed and visibility was severely reduced. The officer in charge of *The Universe* sent a short one-second coded message to his counterpart in command of *Phorcys* on a secure military transmitter. This was to be the night.

Having sent the signal, the next stage of the operation was initiated. Firstly, unknown to the sleeping inmates locked up in their comfy cabins in *The Universe,* all gangways and connecting bulkhead doors including fire exits were quietly welded shut. Next the explosive charges in the keel were switched on and were made ready to receive their remote-control activation just seconds after the collision by airborne SMOG personnel hovering in a helicopter above the ship.

Then, as some of the crew dealt with the charges, others attached a transponder to the exact point on the handrail of mega-cruiser's side at which it had been calculated an impact with *Phorcys* would cause the maximum damage. This unit would transmit a signal to the autopilot control unit on the bridge of *Phorcys* and guide her to that point with extreme accuracy. Now the two massive ships, approaching each other at a combined speed of 48 knots, were locked into an irreversible collision course.

Finally, under cover of darkness and just after midnight, the skeleton SMOG crew left *The Universe* on a couple of Chinooks from two of the four helicopter pads on the vessel.

Three minutes or so later, as *The Universe* sailed ahead straight and true on automatic pilot, the 210,000 tonne *Phorcys* was closing fast on her admidships at 25 knots. As the last of the SMOG crew on *Phorcys* scrambled into her lifeboat and then jettisoned themselves into the sea from her steep 50-degree stern-mounted lifeboat launching ramp with just four seconds to spare, her bow smashed into the *The Universe* and cut her clean in half.

The mathematics had been carefully calculated. The impact angle had been a critical part of the calculation. Approaching at 45 degrees, *Phorcys* had added to her effective impact speed because *The Universe* was moving at 23 knots towards her. By coming in at such an angle rather than at 90 degrees, which would have deflected some of the force of the collision, she had added another 23 knots to the force of the collision.

The 210,000 tonne container ship hitting the right point of *The Universe* at a combined speed of 48 knots was more than enough to sever the 524,000 tonne mega-cruiser in two like a hot knife passing through soft butter.

Two Royal Navy helicopters were hovering close overhead to film the epic collision for broadcast on the TV news. The patchy fog ensured that just enough detail was recorded while leaving the press and viewers in no doubt that the weather conditions were largely responsible for the freak collision.

What the viewers could not see were the remotely detonated underwater explosions which ripped the entire keels out of both sections of *The Universe* and caused her to sink under the waves in a matter of seconds while the cameras continued to film, giving credence to the planned claim that there had not been time to evacuate any of the prisoners or most of the crew.

Because every disaster must have some survivors, a carefully staged 'rescue' of eight of the SMOG men was filmed. At a safe distance from the actual collision location, some of the crew from *Phorcys'* lifeboat jumped into the sea just under a Royal Navy rescue helicopter, while their colleagues sped away in the lifeboat to scuttle it with explosive charges before being picked up themselves. Later the dramatic camera footage of the men being winched from the sea would be reported as the rescue of the only survivors of the crew of *The Universe.*

While the two separate halves of *The Universe* had sunk in a matter of seconds, *Phorcys* on the other hand, although badly damaged at the bow, was still afloat. The sea around her was littered with dozens of shipping containers, which had their retaining straps shorn in the impact. However, as her engines were in the stern and therefore had been undamaged by the collision, she was still under power and heading on the same course, although she had lost speed due to the collision.

At this point, however, the unmanned 210,000-tonne cargo ship was a dangerous liability and control of her had to be regained.

Once again, it was time for some staged drama – a daring raid by SBS commandos to retake the *Phorcys* from its captors. The cover story was going to be that the Somali pirates, being unprofessional seaman, must have lost their way in the fog. Furthermore, evidently they must have been unfamiliar with both the safety equipment aboard *Phorcys*, which would normally have prevented such a collision, and the standard safety procedures at sea in conditions of poor visibility. The fact that they had run straight into *The Universe* would be largely attributed to these two failings.

The explanation for why the pirates had ventured so far from Somalia was to be that anti-piracy intelligence sources believed that they had hidden out in the Atlantic to avoid detection while negotiating a handover of *The Universe* to her Norwegian owners. Presumably they had intended to sail her to a rendezvous point once this had been arranged, and then make their way home in a smaller nondescript vessel provided by the owners as part of a handover-at-sea-while-in-neutral-international-waters-type deal, which was becoming more common in piracy hijacks.

This story would be possible for the press to corroborate with the Norwegian owners of *Phorcys* later, because since the SMOG captured her they had been in faux negotiations with the owners during which it had been agreed that the 'pirates' would bring the ship to a rendezvous point in the Atlantic for the exchange. Because they assumed that they were dealing with genuine pirates, the owners saw nothing unusual in these demands.

The explanation of why *The Universe* had been unable to avoid the collision was to be blamed on the unwieldiness of the gigantic vessel, and more importantly on the fact that the radar system had developed a fault. The captain would testify that he had been forced to slow down the vessel and continuously transmit his position to other ships in the area as he and his crew had effectively been without radar. Obviously the pirates had not taken heed of these safety warnings, again, presumably due to their lack of expertise in the operation of the radio equipment on the *Phorcys*.

The great thing about pirates is of course that they can be shot dead in a raid to retake a vessel and no one bats an eyelid, and dead pirates are then not around to give their side of the story. With this in mind, further dramatic film footage was produced from Royal Navy helicopters covering a daring boarding 'raid' of the empty ship in which it was later claimed the miscreant pirate crew had all been killed.

To add authenticity to the story, the SBS men 'raiding' the ship fired live rounds into the bridge to leave some nice bullet holes for the ship's owners to coo over when it was returned later into their extremely grateful hands.

They fired bursts from their own Heckler & Koch MP5 9mm submachine guns into the ship's doors, windows and bulkheads, and also bursts from the 7.62 AK 47s, which they had left on board from the original hijack. They had been armed with the AK47s when they staged the pirate raid on the ship, because these were the normal weapons of Somali pirates.

The raiders deliberately also left lots of empty shell casings from both types of weapons on the decks to be found by the owners later. They even broke open small sachets of real human blood to leave stains on the deck of the bridge and other areas of the ship. These sachets of blood, each from a different individual, had been surreptitiously acquired from a Somali hospital blood bank and had then been stored in a fridge on the *Phorcys* since the hijack in order to cover the possibility of any future DNA analysis of the stains by post-collision investigators.

The helicopters hovering overhead filmed the muzzle flashes of the SBS weapons as well as the ultra-bright flashes of the stun grenades thrown all over the ship by the commandos during supposed fire fights with the pirates. It all looked very dramatic, especially when realistic body bags full of heavy dummies supposedly containing the corpses of the pirates were dragged out onto the deck in full view of the cameras.

Later it was claimed that as the Somali pirates were Muslims, they were buried at sea right away in respect for the tradition of their faith, which calls for burial within twenty-four hours. Handy that.

The floating shipping containers now littering the sea around *Phorcys* formed part of a UN aid shipment, ironically destined for Somalia. They contained large quantities of grain and foodstuffs in addition to some agricultural vehicles and equipment such as tractors, quad bikes and trailers. The Royal Navy managed to retrieve about 90 per cent of the more buoyant containers by towing them behind motor launches and some of the smaller ships in the escort fleet.

Once alongside the container vessel, they reloaded them over the low gunnels of *Phorcys* and back onto her decks by using her multiple on-board crane systems, which ran along overhead gantries covering the entire length of the deck-loading area. This system was one of the new innovations to be installed on the latest container ships for the very purpose of recovering containers at sea. However, as this massive retrieval operation lasted four days, inevitably some containers simply vanished over the horizon.

A substantial quantity of these missing containers ended up on the coasts of Ireland, Cornwall and Devon. The ones that arrived had mostly been those overlooked by the Royal Navy due to the fact that, as they contained the heavy agricultural vehicles, they had floated lower in the water and so were harder to spot than those containing foodstuffs, which floated higher. However, being hermetically sealed, they had not sunk on their long journey back to land, nor were their contents damaged by seawater.

Irrespective of their final landing destination, whenever the officers from the coastguard or local police arrived to retrieve them from the beaches, they always discovered them empty. It was quite remarkable how quickly the tractors, quad bikes and other valuable agricultural equipment had dispersed into the Irish, Cornish and Devonshire countryside, never to be seen or heard of again by the authorities.

The insurance company underwriting *The Universe* was extremely grateful to the Royal Navy for rescuing her intact and saving them from paying the £50-million ransom demanded by the 'pirates'.

A press conference was held by the insurance company, at which I was present. The company's chairman enthused about the Royal Navy in his speech and praised their professionalism.

When it came to the time for my reply, I suggested that as they had saved so much money, it might be a nice gesture if his company underwrote a second shipment of aid to Somalia, and perhaps with twice as many tractors and agricultural machinery this time to make up for the ones that were lost. In the glare of the world's press, the insurance company chairman had little choice but to agree.

It was announced on the news that the eight 'survivors' of the supposed Royal Naval crew from the stricken mega-cruiser *The Universe* had escaped death only because they were on the bridge or upper area of the ship at the time of the impact. It was stated that a further one-hundred-and-eighty-three men who were supposedly guarding the prisoners were tragically drowned along with them. But of course, in line with normal Armed Forces policy, their names would not be released until their relatives had been informed.

It was announced a few weeks later on the TV news channels that the 'relatives' of the one-hundred-and-eighty-three 'deceased servicemen' had decided that in view of the nature of the tragedy they would prefer the names of their loved ones to remain anonymous and that the media were going to respect their wishes.

In view of the surviving captain's 'testimony' concerning the faulty radar system aboard *The Universe*, I placed blame on the ship's owners for failing to ensure that the preproduction vessel was as fully seaworthy as they had assured me it was. I paid them the initial £10-million deposit but as the ship had not completed the journey under the terms of the contract they were not entitled to any more.

Unsurprisingly, once the public got over the initial shocking news, which took less than twenty-four hours as the voyage had been deliberately timed to take place during the first week of the

World Cup, the general population did not appear to shed a single tear.

This was particularly so once the benefit to the economy had been explained. This was done on a TV news channel, almost as if it was an afterthought, as in 'Well, actually, come to think of it, there is a bright side to this terrible tragedy.' This was followed a couple of weeks later by the presentation of a detailed plan as to how the annual £87.6-billion saving would be reallocated to reduce NHS waiting times and build new hospitals.

A few lefty liberal human rights types started to bang on about how irresponsible it had been to put all the prisoners on the same ship. However, once it was pointed out to them that this luxurious mega-cruiser would have normally accommodated the rich elite, 15,000 of whom would presumably also have drowned, they couldn't then agree with each other whether this was a good or a bad thing and therefore how to respond, and so decided to shut up.

Predictably a few of the relatives of the prisoners were a little voracious, but not all of them by any means. Some of the married ones seemed quite relieved to be rid of their troublesome spouses. Ultimately, though, the fuss soon died down as no one was interested in listening to them, and anyway I ensured that none of the media would give them any airtime or print space.

The Cuban government was understandably somewhat miffed initially. However, I heard soon after that they had negotiated an even more lucrative deal with the Americans to fill the smart new jails with some of the US white-collar-crime prisoners, part of which arrangement included handing back Guantanamo Bay. This in turn has led to a significant thawing of the stand-off between Cuba and the USA.

I also heard that Bernie Madoff is doing very well on one of the Cuban prison farms now, having established an agricultural collective scheme which involves prisoners and guards investing a bag of potatoes with him, for which they receive several new potatoes back every month at an annual rate of return representing 18 per cent.

As a gesture of consolation on behalf of Britain, I offered the Cubans £10,000 a head per annum for a doctor and £20,000 for any top specialist who wanted to come and work in the NHS in addition to the normal doctor's salary they would receive here, some of which would inevitably find its way back into the Cuban economy.

I became their new best dictator again instantly but I did have to calm them down a bit when they offered me half a million of them.

So the prison ship cruise, what a result! A criminal-free Britain and over £87.6 billion a year saved to be put to far better use in doubling the National Health budget for a one-off investment of just £10 million and the cost of a little bit of fuel used by the Royal Navy.

Not only this, but now, without a criminal fraternity to justify their existence and pay their inflated wages, the power base of the PCB has received the first of many mortal blows. Soon this island and its people will be free from their evil influence for ever.

Prison Ship Cruise, oh yes, really GTJD.

Chapter seven

Roads and Driving

The policies I instigated to get Britain moving faster and safer were divided into four key areas.

1. Traffic-flow policy
2. Policing the roads
3. Driver training
4. Road signs and layout

Unlike the previous minister of transport or apparently any of his brain-dead department, I realised that a key factor to a happier and more prosperous Britain was to improve traffic flow. Less frustration and more efficiency lead to more prosperity and a happier, less stressed population. To achieve this, several practical changes needed to be implemented, all of them based on pure common sense, a quality lacking in all politicians, particularly cabinet members.

Roadworks

Under my new regime, all temporary roadworks on motorways have by law to incorporate electronic signs which inform motorists whether there are *actually* any workers on site or not. If they *are* on site, electronic speed signs indicate a maximum speed of 50 m.p.h. controlled by average-speed cameras. However, when no workers are on site, the signs switch to 70 m.p.h., which due to the potentially hazardous presence of the cones, is still under the new 90 m.p.h. motorway speed limit I have introduced, but fast enough to ease traffic congestion. Drivers are politely and continuously reminded via flashing electronic lights that within the defined zone this speed is monitored by the average-speed cameras.

My view was that motorists in the past have never objected to driving at 50 m.p.h. when workers *were* actually on site, but they did get thoroughly fed up with being held up by completely unnecessary speed limits for months or often *years* on end when no work was in progress, which up until now, has been the case for 99 per cent of the time.

£10 per cone per day

This has proved an excellent new policy. To help the 'empty road-works' syndrome situation further, I also passed a law making it illegal to erect and leave coned areas on a motorway for more than one week without workers on site. Fines are based on £10 per cone left for any twenty-four-hour period. Any delay in finishing a roadworks project would now cost contractors hundreds of thousands per month.

Once in place the impact of this law on traffic flow was instantaneous. It was remarkable to note how quickly road works that had previously lain untouched for months and even years in some cases, suddenly got completed.

Accidents

Motorway accidents cost the country a vast amount of money, possibly as much as £1 million a time when the impact of delays to business is taken into consideration. Until my changes, the practice had always been to put the needs of the police and the accident investigation agencies first and the road users last. In my view unless deaths are involved, which in the vast majority of cases they are not, this is totally unjustifiable.

In contrast, I remember arriving at the scene of an accident on an elevated mountain section of a northern Italian autostrada while on holiday there in the 1990s and being highly impressed by the sight of an Italian police twin-rotor-bladed Chinook helicopter clamping a massive electromagnet to the top of the crashed cars and then simply dumping them over the edge of the elevated road to fall several hundred feet to the bottom of a ravine for collection later, presumably having first ensured the occupants had been removed, but you never know with the Italian police.

That wonderful display of GTJD, gave me the inspiration for a new policy on motorway accidents, code name FIMITA, short for Flow Is More Important Than Accidents.

FIMITA

Under FIMITA, first responders on the scene must always be motorcycle-mounted police and paramedics who quickly assess whether serious medical attention is required. If it is, helicopter-based emergency services arrive on the scene within a few short minutes from permanently staffed rapid response air ambulance and airborne fire service rescue units located all over the motorway network. These airborne units land right on the motorway and quickly cut the seriously injured out of the wrecks and whisk them away to hospital.

Where minor injuries are involved, to keep costs down, the paramedics treat the victims at the side of the motorway until conventional ambulances reach them. Should they freeze and get wet while they wait, that's just a bonus in my view. Maybe next time they will pay more attention to their driving.

Except in very exceptional circumstances, such as a multiple pile-up involving more than four vehicles, or actual fatalities, my new policy calls for a maximum acceptable delay of twenty minutes for the dead or seriously injured to be removed from the scene and for traffic to start flowing again.

Equally importantly, the second the injured have been removed from the vehicles, the police must put their Land Rover Discoveries to a more useful purpose than to provide them with a comfortable warm place to sit and drink coffee. They are now obliged to use them to pull the crashed vehicles off the carriageway and onto the hard shoulder without any regard to the further damage this might cause, in order to facilitate the much greater priority, which is get the traffic flowing again.

A new change to the laws with regard to motor insurance results in insurance companies being unable to recover costs from the police or emergency services for any damage caused by moving a crashed vehicle off the road. If it was so damaged that it needed to be towed off the road, what the hell do a few more dents and scratches matter?

FIMITA is in stark contrast to the old policy, which was to keep the entire motorway network of Britain waiting for at least an hour for the accident assessment team to turn up and then a further hour while they photograph every inch of road, even if the incident simply involved a couple of old ladies who, having fallen asleep in the slow lane, gently collided with each other and cracked an indicator lens.

My view was that if there has been an accident, two or three minutes of photography by trained first responders is all the evidence that is required to do a post-mortem on who was to blame.

Ultimately however, except where death has occurred, deciding who or what was to blame should *never* take precedence over holding up thousands of innocent drivers and causing the subsequent financial and social consequences of missed business appointments, ruined holidays, missed flights, screaming family arguments, divorces and traumatised young children and dogs empting their bladders on the back seat.

FIMTA has proved deeply unpopular with the police accident investigators who loved all the overtime pay they got for standing around doing bugger all for hours while laughing at the stranded motorists. But in line with the vast majority of my policies, it has proved extremely popular with the general public.

FIMTA, good plan then, GTJD.

HGVs

It is now illegal for heavy goods vehicles to travel between 8 a.m. on a Saturday morning and 6 a.m. on a Monday. This new policy does not disrupt the UK infrastructure at all as all main trunk distribution to Royal Mail depots, courier depots and supermarket hubs can still be delivered by the normal time on a Saturday morning.

The vast majority of further distribution after that time has always traditionally been facilitated by smaller vans anyway, so why HGVs were ever allowed to clutter up the roads causing unnecessary congestion at weekends when the roads are carrying a much higher volume of private cars is a mystery to me.

If you ever needed proof that there wasn't a politician with a single brain cell at the Department of Transport before I took over, then that is it.

Now weekend traffic congestion is massively reduced and HGV drivers are more relaxed, happy people, as they know that they cannot be forced to work at weekends any longer. All transport companies must provide cars or motorcycles at main depots for HGV drivers to return home or, alternatively, public transport passes.

Any driver of an HGV caught travelling outside designated hours without reasonable proof that it was unavoidable due to something such as a breakdown, will be subject to an on-the-spot fine of £1,000. A wilful second offence leads to a twelve-month driving ban.

Caravans and trailers

It is also now illegal for caravans or any trailers to travel on the road network between midnight on a Thursday and midnight on Sunday for the same reasons as the HGVs. Similar £1,000 on-the-spot fines are imposed for wilful disobedience. Second-time offenders have their caravans or trailers crushed without compensation and are banned by law from towing anything ever again by a permanent modification to their driving licences.

A few horsey types who can't afford lorries, might have to turn up a bit earlier at the local hunt point–to-points or gymkhanas now, but that gives them the excuse to spend another couple of nights away from home shagging the groom in the horsebox, which is the only reason any sane person pretends to be interested in horses, being as they are, the highest maintenance, most neurotic, fragile and terminally brainless animals on the planet.

Policing the roads: the great lie about speed

For decades the lazy traffic police departments, backed up by dishonest politicians, have persuaded the gullible public that the main reason for accidents on the open road is excess speed. Urban areas aside, this is propagandist claptrap.

Time and time again, claims that excess speed is the single most significant cause of serious road accidents has been force-fed to the public. The totally untrue statistic, which has repeatedly been quoted over the decades by politicians and some elements of the police alike, is that excess speed is the major contributory factor in *30 per cent* of accidents. The road-accident records tell a very different story.

Way back in the 1980s, an independent examination of the police accident records clearly showed that this 30 per cent figure was totally untrue and the real figure was closer to 4 per cent. Even as late as 2000, an examination of the Transport Research Laboratory's report, TRL Report 323, showed that the claim reported by the government of the time that speed 'was a major contributory factor in about a *third* of all road accidents' was totally fabricated.

In fact the *actual* figure shown in the TRL 323 report that they were quoting, as you can determine for yourself if you google it, was nowhere near 30 per cent, but really 7.3 per cent, with only 4.5 per cent being cited as the definite cause of the accident.

Not only that, but of that 4.5 per cent of accidents actually reported by the police as being genuinely attributable to excess speed, the report showed that only three out of ten of these happened in excess of national speed limits. So in 70 per cent of cases, drivers were not even breaking the speed limit. So really only 1.35 per cent were caused by illegal speeding.

This is a very long way from 30 per cent. In short, the propaganda fed to us about excess speed being the main cause of accidents on the open road over the last forty or fifty years has always been total bollocks.

Even more worryingly, in 2004 the Highways Agency began to suspect that because so many more *new* accidents were occurring on camera sites, the presence of cameras themselves might in fact be distracting drivers' attention from the road or causing them to make sudden braking manoeuvres, both of which were leading to *more* rather than *fewer* serious accidents.

They were concerned enough to commission a secret report called TRL Report 595 to examine the impact of fixed cameras on roads. Shockingly, this report indicated that far from saving lives, where fixed cameras were installed on road works, the risk of accidents resulting in injury was *increased* by 55 per cent, and where they were installed on motorways, the risk *increased* by 31 per cent. Hardly surprising then that TRL Report 595 was ordered to remain secret and never to see the light of day.

I had always suspected there had been an underhand conspiracy between politicians and certain elements of the police when it came to blaming speed for the majority of accidents. It was only when my research team gained access to the real information, hidden away in the secret government archives, that my suspicions were confirmed.

I have driven over a million miles on British roads and none of the accidents that I have ever witnessed, including fatal ones, were caused by excess speed. Quite the opposite, often the accidents I have witnessed were caused by people driving too slowly and holding traffic up; a classic example would be drivers pulling caravans and creating queues of traffic stretching out to miles. This congestion causes frustration and ultimately encourages ill-judged overtaking by highly stressed drivers of other vehicles, frequently with fatal results.

The concept that it is acceptable for one selfish driver to hold up hundreds of others during peak periods is totally insane. My new regulations concerning legal travel times for caravans and trailers have proved massively effective in cutting road casualties, which would have been incorrectly and dishonestly recorded as being due to excess speed under the old regime.

Once again, if the Department of Transport and the traffic police had really cared about saving lives, they would have implemented a policy like mine decades ago. The fact that they did not is just another example of their outrageous hypocrisy.

However, now that I knew for sure that my hunch about the true statistics was correct, I certainly was not prepared to let the situation continue. As soon as I took over, I made some serious changes to road safety policy. I was determined to make the police do something they have never done before, to actually *police* the roads properly rather than hide behind dishonest propaganda and their conviction-generating electronic speed traps.

Speed *outside of urban areas*, has *provably* never been the *most* significant factor in accident causation. The real reasons why individual drivers cause accidents are the three *C*s, or rather the lack of them, which are:

Concentration
Consideration
Competence

When I lived in Germany for a while, my average daily commuting speed in my Aston Martin Vantage was 134 m.p.h., and on my Triumph Daytona motorbike, 127 m.p.h. Never once did I come close to having an accident in tens of thousands of miles of driving this daily 55-mile commute, nor did any of my fellow travellers driving at high speed quite legally on a daily basis.

Why do the German authorities allow this? Is it because the German government believe its population are better drivers than the British or because they are prepared to trust them more?

Contrary to myth, it certainly is not because the German autobahns are better in terms of design or condition than our roads; they are for the main part nowhere near as good as our motorways, often nothing more than worn-out old concrete-topped dual carriageways.

When Italy raised the speed limit on its autostradas in the 1990s, fatal accidents fell by nearly 20 per cent because the higher speeds forced people to concentrate more, show more consideration to others, even if this was for the selfish motivation of their own survival, and gain more competence.

Following this example, my first change to the traffic laws was to raise the speed limit to 90 m.p.h. on motorways, 80 m.p.h. on dual carriageways and 70 m.p.h. on *most*, but *not all* single carriageways. With 10 per cent tolerance but with a £50 fine per 1 m.p.h. over the ten percent and a one-month ban for every extra 10 m.p.h.

I did not believe that the general population was ready for *unlimited* speed on motorways just yet, after so many years of it being 70 m.p.h. If I were to remain in charge for longer than my five-year term, I would gradually increase the speed limit by 10 m.p.h. at a time every three years or so until eventually it was unlimited. For now, however, raising the limit by 20 m.p.h. to 90 m.p.h. helped both traffic flow and to raise drivers' concentration and situational awareness.

A-class drivers

I introduced an incentive for people to drive better. If any individual voluntarily attends a new highly advanced driving course run by ex-police class 1 driving instructors and manages to achieve a pass mark of at least 85 per cent, they are then allowed to display a special A-shaped hologram badge on their car or motorcycle, which allows them to exceed the open-road speed limits *outside of urban areas* by 20 per cent.

Anyone caught masquerading as a A-class driver by attempting to use another person's badge as a excuse to speed receives a £1,000 fine and a five-year ban, plus the badge owner losses his A-class privileges for life for allowing the badge to be used.

Fairer points system

Also in the vein of encouraging better driving, the points endorsement system is now fairer. For every six years a person has driven without any points, he or she is let off the first three points they would have otherwise received, although all fines still apply.

Once fined, they have to drive for another six years without collecting points to receive the same benefit again. This policy has appealed to the natural sense of fairness in the British psyche and so was welcomed by motorists and has led to better relationship between them and the traffic police.

Points are also now removed from display on licences after three years, the irritating fourth 'display only' year having been outlawed.

Paper Licences

Paper licences are no longer required. They were pointless anyway and only assisted identity theft. All points information is stored electronically on the photo-carrying plastic licences, along with other vital information such as place and date of birth. None of this information is now openly displayed as part of my new programme to combat identity theft (see later chapter on this topic).

Doing away with totally unnecessary paper licences saves the country £4.5 million per year, which I reallocated to my rural pub bus programme, which I will mention in a minute.

Road tax

There are some changes to road tax classes and costs.

Motorcycles under 1,200cc are road tax exempt as they make a positive contribution to relieving congestion. Motorcycles over 1,200cc pay £200 per annum as the majority of bikes in this category are large cruisers that do nothing to ease congestion as they are as slow and cumbersome and occupy as much road space as a small car. Also, as their engines are the same size as that of a small car, they should be taxed like one, especially as they are generally less fuel-efficient.

Electric vehicles actually make no positive impact on the general environment because they simply transfer the CO_2 down the road to the nearest coal-fired power station generating the electricity to charge their batteries.

Hybrids make no greater a positive impact on the environment than many conventional fuel-efficient cars and in fact, due to the largely unsustainable resources required to build their batteries, like the electric cars, have a much larger net negative impact.

These two vehicle groups are therefore now taxed at £200 per annum.

Other vehicles are divided into groups and taxed according to their fuel efficiency. The most economical vehicle pays £200 per annum, the least economical pays £400.

There is a rolling-forward road tax exemption for vehicles over 25 years old, and for all Aston Martins on the basis that they make an important aesthetic contribution to the environment.

No, not really, just kidding about that one.

Camera vans and Gatso cameras

Covert partnership camera vans at the side of the road are now banned as they were robotic and did not take into account perfectly safe and responsible driving such as a driver temporarily exceeding the speed limit to overtake a line of traffic or taking swift and sensible action to avoid a collision.

Only the police are allowed to issue fines for driving too fast but they are now allowed to erect speed traps only at accident black spots where excess speed has been proved to be a genuine factor in causing accidents and only irresponsible drivers would be driving too fast.

The police are no longer allowed to use lame excuses such as the existence of an accident black spot a mile or so down the road to set up a speed trap on a perfectly safe piece of dual carriageway on a dry, sunny day in order to get easy convictions to make up for their lack of impact on genuine crime and to conceal their lack of interest in actually doing anything significant to improve road safety.

If it turns out the police have set up a speed trap in a location not in accordance with these rules, it can now be retrospectively declared illegal. The relevant police division then has to pay back every fine issued even if they did not receive the money themselves and all convictions from that site are overturned.

I can tell you that a few such cases soon refocused the police into acting more responsibly and honestly.

Outside of urban areas, Gatso cameras can now operate only in genuine accident black spots where, again, speed has been proven to be a genuine factor in accidents. As this is the case in only a fraction of them, because the average speed of an accident at a UK black spot is just 41 m.p.h., there are now very few cameras on the open road.

Instead the Gatsos have been recycled to urban areas where excess speed actually *is* the largest cause of accidents and therefore where they can do some good.

Black-spot policing

So instead of setting speed traps on the open road several miles away from the accident black spots and using their coincidental existence on the same road as the excuse for doing so, it is now the responsibility of the police to regularly monitor the *actual* local black spots in their area and pull serious offenders over and show them video evidence of their unsafe driving, which is filmed via cameras mounted in the police vehicles. If appropriate, they can then slap them with a £150 fine and points and even in some cases issue them with a licencse suspension pending retraining.

Urban speed limits

In the urban environment, in total contrast to the open road, excess speed is without doubt the most significant cause of accidents, due to the close proximity of pedestrians, cyclists, dogs and so forth to moving vehicles. So a radical shake-up of urban speed limits was necessary to prevent drivers losing concentration and situational awareness. Again, *unlike* the open road, in the urban environment, speed cameras *are* a highly effective method of implementing this, providing they are used in conjunction with variable speed limits.

So urban speed limits are now electronically variable and therefore more relevant and sensible. Outside schools, electronic speed signs are mounted openly and highly visibly to the rear of bright yellow Gatso cameras. These display different speeds at various times. At pick-up and drop-off times the speed limit drops to 10 m.p.h., with zero tolerance from the Gatso cameras. For the rest of the day outside schools and other places like hospitals, park entrances and old people's homes, they display 20 m.p.h., with zero tolerance.

The normal urban speed limit is 30 m.p.h., but now this is also enforced by 10-per-cent-tolerance Gatso cameras mounted on every sign. These have been recycled from their totally unnecessary locations on the open road so there are plenty to go around.

So 34 m.p.h. now carries a £150 fine and three points. In certain places with high pedestrian traffic, electronic signs can also display lower speeds at peak times.

Where zero tolerance is in force, its application is *clearly and continuously* displayed with flashing signs in the interest of fairness and effective enforcement.

Urban dual carriageway speed limits

Conversely however, on dual carriageway sections entering or leaving cities, where barriers protect pedestrians on both sides, the speed limit can vary according to conditions and can, via the electronic signs, be raised from 40 m.p.h. to as high as 60 m.p.h. at certain peak times to ease traffic flow. Due to the higher speeds, these limits carry 10 per cent tolerance.

Drinking and driving

In this particular area of law all the existing regulations still apply. However, I have introduced some practical improvements.

Pub minibus scheme

The first is that generous grants are now available for any pub landlord in an urban area who wishes to purchase a minibus to drive his clientele home at closing time, along with an annual fuel and part-time driver allowance.

Rural pub bus scheme

In rural areas I have used the money from doing away with paper licences to sponsor a special pub pick-up and delivery minibus service specifically to call in at all village centres and pubs in a 25-mile radius every night. Every pub on the round is visited from 7 p.m. onwards at least once and then always again at closing time, by law. Where practical, drinkers are also picked up and dropped off at or close to their houses.

Farmers using this service generally leave a vehicle at the end of their farm lanes, so that when the bus drops them off at the top of these, they can make their way home safely on their own land well off the main road.

This service has made a massive impact on reducing rural drink-driving accidents. The programme has also helped many rural pubs stay open and has reduced rural suicides due to loneliness.

Drink-driving police division

Now there are no more criminals, the police have more time on their hands, so I thought they might as well make themselves useful. I formed a new unit of the traffic police that, at the request of any citizen who wants to know if they have consumed too much alcohol or Charlie to drive home, drops by the pub or club and tests them. In most cities DD police units are based in pub car parks at closing time so drinkers can voluntarily approach them.

The DD officer tests all the occupants wishing to travel in the vehicle. If they test clear, they are voluntarily frisked for alcohol and drugs and the vehicle is inspected, too, using electronic alcohol and drug detection equipment. The officer then witnesses the occupants climbing into the vehicle and sticks paper seals across all the doors and windows, and issues them with a certificate, which displays both the time and location at which it was given. Should a traffic policeman stop them later, it will be evident if they did in fact drive straight home or if they went to another bar.

The deal is simple: if they drive straight home without breaking any of the paper seals on the doors and windows, they are immune from further test. If they are caught attempting to exploit the free pass, they have any sentence and driving ban doubled.

This common-sense policy has encouraged people to voluntarily test themselves when leaving licensed premises, and in conjunction with the Pub Minibus Scheme, has resulted in a reduction of DD-linked accidents by over 74 per cent.

Cyclists

Cyclists are now required by law to wear a high-visibility bib with a unique registration number, which is registered exclusively to them on an individual basis like a car registration plate. They are also issued with a photo ID cycling licence, obtained by passing a cycle proficiency test, which must be on display in a transparent pocket on the front of their bib at all times.

It was notable that after introduction of this test, only 34 per cent of cyclists passed on the first attempt. Failure to wear a registration bib while cycling results in confiscation of the cycle, irrespective of its value, and a £250 fine.

This policy allows the police to bring to book those who are in my opinion the worst hooligans in the urban environment. Riding on a pavement results in cycle confiscation and a £150 fine. Crossing a road junction on red lights results in confiscation and the same fine.

Now that they can be caught on the zero-tolerance Gatsos, they can also be fined for speeding exactly like a car driver or motor-cyclist and receive points on the same basis, with twelve points leading to disqualification. If they do not have a driving licence, the points are added to their cycle licence on the same basis.

Injuring a pedestrian with a cycle while riding it on a pavement is an automatic six-month jail sentence subject to Double Up, in addition to losing the right to be issued with a registration bib for a further two years.

Skate boards, roller-skates and push scooters

It is now illegal to use skateboards or roller-skates outside of designated areas in public parks. Anyone caught using them either on the pavement or on the public road is dragged to an ATM machine, forced to pay a fine of £150 and has the board or skates confiscated. If they don't have a credit card on them they are held in custody at a police station until the fine is paid.

This new policy has resulted in several roller-skaters having to walk home in their socks, which is a real bonus.

The same policy goes for push scooters, whether ridden by children or adults. Parents receive the fine in the case of children.

Injuring a pedestrian on a pavement with any of these abominable devices brings an automatic six-month jail sentence as per bicycles, and is subject to Double Up.

Motorway lane hogging

The police now have to spend more time on motorways actually policing dangerous and inconsiderate driving rather than speed. For example, any driver driving slowly in the middle or fast lane of a motorway while inconsiderately holding up traffic receives a £150 fine on the spot, is required to attend a driving course and has his or her licence suspended until a satisfactory pass grade is achieved.

Motorcycle-gang congestion

Motorcycles are my favourite mode of transport but I hate seeing slow cruisers crawling along in large gangs, blocking normal traffic. So now there is a motorcycle-gang congestion law. This applies to the likes of those irritating groups of middle-aged Harley riders who clutter up the motorway system as they crawl noisily along at 50–60 m.p.h. with their massive leather-clad wives on the back blocking the view ahead.

It is now illegal for more than three motorcycles to travel together in a group closer than half a mile apart on a motorway or for any motorcycle to travel *under* 70 m.p.h. on a motorway except in adverse weather conditions.

Roundabouts

Any driver stopping unnecessarily at a clearly empty roundabout and treating it as a junction receives a £150 fine and driving-test requirement. Again, the police now have to regularly monitor particularly busy roundabouts at peak traffic periods to deal with offenders.

Driver training

The priority here was to reduce the carnage among young, inexperienced drivers, particularly young males under twenty-five, the wholesale slaughter of whom, apart from being a terrible tragedy, I consider a costly and quite avoidable waste of expensive education.

Driver training is therefore now a compulsory subject in school, which starts at twelve years old. Secondary-level pupils are taught the concept of hazard awareness and forward observation via super-realistic video driving games, while sitting in simulators with functioning and properly weighted steering wheels and controls.

Sponsored by the motor insurance industry

There is a national pre-test driving championship open to all pupils, which is now compulsorily sponsored by the motor insurance industry. For pupils of seventeen plus, the top prize is a new car and three years' free insurance, second prize is three years' free insurance and so forth. Younger children are able to accumulate insurance discount points over six years of consistently high scores on the video games, which can be claimed when they start driving.

The training is also practical from the outset. Disused airfields have been converted into driver-training facilities where pupils learn car control and accident-avoidance techniques in special vehicles fitted with rally harnesses and roll cages.

National Car Control Championship

Driver training becomes progressively more advanced as the pupils become older and covers skid control on ice, wet roads, mud and simulated snow. Again, at higher levels the opportunity for practical competition exists and a National Car Control Championship ensures that young men in particular actually learn to control cars to a high standard rather than simply believe that they can.

This policy has already brought the beneficial by-product of creating several future rally champions and some promising young racing drivers. Grants are now available to assist the most talented drivers advance their motorsport career, as a motivation to others.

Cars for learners

A change in the law has resulted in learners being allowed to drive only specially converted cars for a minimum of three years or until they reach their twenty-sixth birthday. Learner-approved cars, which can be of any type or make, must be fitted with roll cages and only a pair of four-point harness rally seats fitted in the front.

Drivers must also wear an open-face rally helmet when driving. The cars are fitted with race-specification fully plumbed fire-extinguishing systems in the cabin and engine bays. These systems are automatically activated by an inertia switch in a serious collision or rollover.

Only one passenger can be carried in the front seat as no rear passengers are allowed, and this front passenger must also wear a helmet and be fully strapped in irrespective of their age. This is due to the safety roll cage, which, while in all other respects is a lifesaving device, could otherwise cause head injury in an accident.

Any young driver caught without a helmet or not fully strapped to his or her seat, or driving with a passenger without either, receives a two-year ban and then a retest.

The vehicles are also fitted with GPS-activated speed limiters, which activate in urban areas and prevent the car from moving at more than 30 m.p.h. This does not protect the driver from fines for failing to observe lower variable urban speed limits.

No music systems of any kind, including iPods with earphones, are allowed to be installed as these distract the driver's attention. That's the official line, but just between you and me, actually it was really to stop them from filling up their empty backseat areas with massive woofers and tweeters and then deafening everyone within a five-mile radius.

This special learner-car policy has so far reduced young deaths and serious life-altering injuries, particularly in the vulnerable young male under-twenty-five category, by 93 per cent, with the useful by-product being a massive saving to the NHS.

Road signs and layout

Signs in this country were appalling until my new policies sorted them out. If the traffic police had really cared about saving road users' lives, they would have demanded an end to such ludicrous road layouts as lane merges on the blind side of hills, which is exactly where 90 per cent of merges used to be before my time.

If there was ever a concrete example of police hypocrisy in regard to road safety, it was in the specific area of road layout and signage.

These indefensible road layouts were killing hundreds of motorists per annum. This was not recognised largely due to the fact that the fatalities were concealed by police anti-speed propaganda, which incorrectly recorded them as being due to excess speed.

In poor weather conditions especially, all it took was a couple of HGVs crawling up a hill to cover the warning signs indicating a merge of lanes ahead, which were inevitably positioned just over the blind side of a hill, to wipe out many an unsuspecting holiday-making family or innocent traveller unfamiliar with the road.

Of course the police loved these dramatic crashes in which everyone died; it was so easy to point to the horribly mangled wrecks on TV later and solemnly claim it was just another example of excess speed. In fact neither unsuspecting family had been driving anywhere near the speed limit when, at just 45–50 m.p.h. each, they came together at 90 or 100 m.p.h. They were simply victims of a murderously irresponsible road-signage system, which defied any logic at all.

Hundreds of lives saved by a bit of paint

My new road-layout regulations have outlawed all merges on the blind side of hills or around blind corners, saving countless lives per year through a bit of common sense and some paint. Creating simple short-distance one-way systems out of existing roads in high-traffic-volume areas has also prevented scores more fatal accidents caused by motorists making quite unnecessary turns across busy main roads and so forth.

Corporate manslaughter for bad road signage

To make sure all this happened promptly, I quickly passed a new law that holds responsible for corporate manslaughter the departments that create signage, if it can be shown their idiotic layout led to the deaths of motorists. This also extended to the regional chief constables who could be charged unless there was strong evidence that they had attempted to do something about it.

This has led to a remarkably different attitude to road layout throughout the country on the part of both road signage departments and police chief constables, resulting in the saving of thousands of lives a year for minimal financial investment.

Britain is moving smoothly

Unsurprisingly, after two years of these policies, the average speed on open roads has increased dramatically with an equally dramatic *decrease* in traffic congestion and with the most significant *reduction* in accidents for fifty years. Open-road accidents have been reduced by 63 per cent now the traffic police actually have to do their job properly and have more time to do so now that crime is virtually non-existent.

The new urban variable speed limits have also cut pedestrian casualties by 87 per cent.

People now drive around much more relaxed, confident in the knowledge that if there is a pile-up on the motorway, the wrecks will be hauled onto the hard shoulder and the broken glass and debris swept off the motorway before the track changes on the radio.

Furthermore, now a British motorist never again has to suffer the indignity of some spotty twenty-three-year-old policeman giving them a patronising lecture about driving too fast on a completely empty, dry dual carriageway on a clear sunny day. Especially as, in contrast to him, who has written off three patrol cars since he joined traffic division eighteen months ago, all paid for by the tax payer, they, perhaps as a doctor or similarly responsible professional, have driven hundreds of thousands of miles without a single accident. Most of these miles will have been driven well in excess of the old national speed limit, but unlike the spotty young cop, safely and sensibly.

Yes, the road users of Britain now drive around with a smile on their faces rather than a scowl and they politely wave each other out of junctions.

Believe it or not, I have even heard reports that some of those ghastly grim-faced, aggressive-looking women living in Surrey and Gloucestershire have cheered up. You know, those awful types who wear too much make-up and tasteless jewellery when they drive spoilt brats with names like Benedict and Candida around in the back of blacked-out Porsche Cayennes. Apparently even some of those have been spotted attempting to smile through their botox.

Actually, come to think of it, maybe that's probably more to do with the extra time they now get in the horsebox with the groom. Yes, Britain is moving smoothly on its roads, GTJD.

Chapter eight

Education

English language

My first objective was to get the English language back. I was sick of watching our own language being progressively replaced by Americanisms and the pseudo-gang culture so-called 'street speak'.

This kind of thing, 'Yo blood, wassup, dude? Like totally bodacious, bro. I'm just, like, chillin' innit?

It is bad enough when you hear it coming from some genuine 'street' moron but when you can't even escape it in your favourite restaurant in Chelsea because there is always some pretentious little public-school trustafarian spouting it, you know things have gone too far.

Even Sacha Baron Cohen's brilliant Ali G character, which satirised this pseudo-street slang has done nothing to diminish its rapid spread into everyday conversation. I suppose the people who talk like this are so thick they probably didn't even realise he was sending them up.

Swearing is a serious cultural problem too. Look, we all swear, I certainly do occasionally, but the truth is that as a nation we swear too much. The F-word and the S-word punctuate almost every sentence now, along with other totally unnecessary additions, such as the word *like* and the even more irritating Americanism *really?* at the end of every sentence.

If you only heard it as you passed through a rough neighbourhood it wouldn't be so bad, but if anything, the higher you go up the food chain the worse the language gets.

I overheard a well-known It girl talking to her vacuous girlfriends in a smart London bar the other day for instance. This is a short example of the distasteful dialogue: 'I mean, *like*, f***ing hell, I just told him, *like*, get your f***ing sh*t together, *like*, what's the f***ing problem? I mean, *like*, f***ing hell, I mean, *like*, sh*t! *Really?*'

One of the her brain-dead entourage replies, '*Like*, sh*t , yaaah, you're, *like*, so f***ing right, I mean, *like*, what the f**k? I mean, sh*t, yaaah. *Like, really?*'

Exactly how and why this utterly moronic conversation modification has developed in the last twenty to thirty years is a mystery. Part of it must be due to the decline in educational standards and discipline. The influence of Hollywood must also have played its part, because in most action films the word *sh★t* punctuates every other sentence. Equally I am sure that our own reality TV productions are also to blame, as they only seem to feature people who use the F-word before every adjective.

One way or another, foul language has been glorified by the entertainment industry on both sides of the Atlantic and therefore sanctioned as an acceptable method of emphasis.

I suppose it is a reflection of how weak-minded and susceptible to brainwashing much of the human race still is.

I thought it was time to put a stop to it. I realised that while I might not be able to do anything about the current generation of brainwashed idiots, at least I could do something about the next.

I needed to employ some teachers with the ability to deprogram the next generation of children and teach them to not only speak and write proper English but also to expand their vocabulary and stop swearing like their cretinous parents.

The problem was that very few teachers could speak or write English properly themselves, and anyway, most were too steeped in political correctness to change, so I needed to bring in outside help.

I needed to parachute an elite rescue squad into the British education system to clean it up, but where would I find these superheroes before I left power?

Once the politically sensitive MPs came back it would be too late. Irrespective of party, they are all far too gutless to deal with something as radical as saving the English language. Too many minorities to offend, too many potential voters to upset.

Actually though, finding the superheroes in time was not that hard. Luckily for my plan, there exists a race whose command of the English language and depth of vocabulary so vastly exceeds our own that it is positively shameful.

I am referring of course to the Irish.

Irish eyes are shining

The Irish officially posses the largest vocabulary of all English-speaking people. How they acquired this is open to debate, some say it is because once they were forced to adopt the English language, and true to their contrary nature, they decided to put one over on the British by speaking it better than them.

Whatever the reason, no one on the planet has a greater command of spoken or written English than an educated Irishman, and so I decided to put the Irish in charge of bringing our language back and saving it from the sewer.

I employed a language professor from University College Dublin and tasked him with recruiting Irish-English language and literature teachers from all over the globe to come and work at all levels from primary school to university. I made sure that the salaries, relocation allowances and expenses offered to the candidates were so ridiculously generous that they were simply too tempting to refuse.

The only condition was that the primary school candidates had to be able to teach without a strong Irish accent. This did not prove an obstacle as the Irish are natural mimics and can quite easily ape a crisp, upper-class, cut-glass English accent if they feel like it.

A few primary school children's parents have been surprised when after several months of exposure to my new Irish teachers, their children have come home not only in possession of a vocabulary much greater in depth and breadth than their own but also sounding like they were born in Buckingham Palace rather than Buckingham Tower Hamlets.

The good old Irish saving the English language, then! Who would have thought it? GTJD.

Discipline

The next problem in need of urgent attention was school discipline. The lack of discipline in schoolchildren and the consequential negative impacts on society as some of them grow up into lawless thugs and psychopaths are entirely the fault of the PCB.

You only have to look at the school shooting massacres that take place in America. None of them are perpetrated by the generations that were properly disciplined as children; all of them come from a generation that has been 'talked to' about their feelings as 'little adults' rather than given a good smack when they stepped out of line.

When I was a teenager, I do not recall a single case in which one of my contemporaries randomly stabbed someone to death in the street, not a single one. Nor for that matter, was there a single case involving one of them shooting another teenager with an illegal handgun. However, before I took over, both such crimes had become commonplace in Britain. At least three such incidents were taking place every month.

This was entirely due to the insane concept of banning corporal punishment and therefore allowing those children born with naturally aggressive dispositions to grow up without a properly reinforced discipline system. The PCB had experimented with changing the natural methodology of discipline, which since the beginning of time has always been based on the threat of, or the occasional actual application of, physically painful punishment.

This entirely natural method has served the human race, and for that matter all other intelligent animals, very well for millions of years. Unsurprisingly this namby-pamby PCB social experiment has very demonstrably failed, with catastrophic and often tragic consequences for those countries which have suffered as a result of its implementation.

This is because the PCB ignored the well-recognised problem, known to mankind since he first swung down from the trees: if you spare the rod you spoil the child.

It's the same with a dog. The happiest, most contended, and emotionally stable dog is one that was properly trained and disciplined as a pup. In other words, given a short, sharp smack when it did something wrong like pee on the carpet. Dogs do not resent this; their mothers give them a quick nip to discipline them, as do the parents of most animals from horses right through to lions. That is how young creatures learn what they should or should not do. Dogs in particular are sociable pack creatures like ourselves, who feel more secure knowing what the rules are.

The neurotic dogs are always the ones owned by old ladies who never smack their little pooches when they do something wrong as pups, as a result of which they never grow out of peeing on the carpet. If you look carefully at them, you will notice that these dogs also spend their lives looking permanently confused and generally quite scared. This is because they are confused; they don't know what is expected of them or what is right or wrong and so they become neurotic.

The problem with humans is that if you don't smack naughty little Daryl as a kid, when he grows up he doesn't pee on the carpet, he ends up stabbing the old lady with the dog in the head with a nine-inch kitchen knife.

Before I sorted the matter out, in some secondary-school classes of mixed-ability children, teachers had to give more attention to the spoilt little thugs than the kids with serious potential. This was an insane situation brought about by the progressive stranglehold of the education system by the namby-pamby PCB.

Well I soon put a stop to all that nonsense. The first thing I did was to repeal the ban on corporal punishment. The second was to send hundreds of CCTV-trained engineers from the Royal Military Engineers, or REME as they are known, into every school in the land over a single weekend and rig covert CCTV cameras in every classroom.

Things were about to change. I was going to restore discipline and I did not give a damn who I upset doing it.

I called the programme, Six of the Best.

Six of the Best

After a week of observing every class in the land on the covert CCTV, it was quite clear who the troublesome children were and, having identified them, on a single Monday in every state school in Britain, they were removed from their normal classes and placed in special classes, which include two extra members of staff in addition to the teachers.

These educational discipline assistants, or EDAs as they are referred to, are large, tough ex-sergeant-major types from the army, and every problem class has two of them now.

The EDAs have carte blanche to clip any obnoxious little brats around the ear as often as is necessary to pull them into line while shouting very loudly at them from about an inch from their nose. I changed the law so that they are immune from prosecution.

Any backchat or cheek directed at the teacher is met with a powerful clout around the ear until it stops. If a class is giving too much trouble for two of these assistants on their own, there are mobile back-up units that bring extra men around to help and then between them they pound some discipline into the worst offenders without any fear of repercussions.

There is now also a strict framework for the discipline beyond clipping them around the ear. I brought back the same points system that existed in the days when I was at school. After three black points for misbehaviour, the miscreants get three strokes with a cane. After three more in the same term they get six strokes. After three more they get six strokes with a split cane, which really hurts – I can remember from personal experience in my prep school days.

Any complaints about ill treatment of the little thugs can now only be referred to the Education Department, which totally ignores them. The change in the law means the police can no longer become involved. However, the department does not get many complaints anyway, due to another change in the law I have made.

This new law holds the parents financially responsible for the cost of disciplining their little brats. Every time a teacher has to clip the ear of little Daryl, the parents are fined £5. When he is canned, it costs them £25 for every three strokes. Failure to pay these fines results in twelve months in prison, as it is now a level 1 crime.

Now when darling little Daryl goes home he also gets clouted by his parents for running up a debt at school. After a couple of months of getting clouted and canned at school and at home, he falls into line, especially as he can no longer play truant.

The police, who have no crime to worry about now, have plenty of resources to round up kids out of school. So instead of just driving by in their patrol cars as the truants set fire to bus shelters because they were terrified of being prosecuted themselves as in the old days, they are now authorised to throw them in the back of a secure van as roughly as they like and deliver them to school in handcuffs if necessary.

This process is made easier by the fact that persistent truants like Daryl have to wear GPS ankle bracelets so the police are alerted the moment one of them is not in school. Of course these electronic devices also make the miscreant very easy to find quickly.

The penalties for truancy are severe. Parents are fined £150 every time it happens and Daryl himself gets six strokes with a split cane in front of the entire school at morning assembly. The sight of that soon discourages others from copying him.

Following the first year of a return to proper discipline, there was not a single trouble-making child to be found in a class in any school throughout the country, and zero truancy. Now there's a surprise.

Most importantly, though, when Daryl grows up, he will not go around stabbing old ladies in the head because all his life he has been told by some namby-pamby PCB liberal loony that it is fine for him to express his anger however and whenever he feels like it and that no one else in the entire world matters but darling psychopathic little Daryl himself.

University education

Traditionally students take a gap year or 'gap yaah' as it is pronounced. Well I had an idea about that.

What I have done is introduce a new updated form of voluntary national service. Wait for it – don't anticipate the order – it's not so draconian as it sounds. The idea is that students voluntarily spend three months in basic training, learning such incredibly useful life skills as personal fitness, survival skills, team-building, leadership skills, communication skills, para-medicine, cooking, orienteering without a GPS, parachuting, skiing, mountaineering, weapons handling, gliding, water-skiing, vehicle maintenance, basic house maintenance, and such skills as how to clean and press clothes properly and so forth. In fact, a hundred fun things they would never otherwise get a chance to try, at least not for free and all at once, plus a hundred other practical skills, which will be useful to them in their future lives.

After the three months' basic training, most of which is very far from dull, and a lot more exciting than the average 'gap yaah' was ever going to be, they then spend three months of even more exciting fun in each of the services, army, navy and air force. At least one of these quarters will be spent on overseas deployment in a non-combat zone.

Free university tuition and books

In return for this year they receive free university tuition and a very adequate textbook allowance in the form of a debit card, which can only be used to buy books and tuition equipment from authorised suppliers.

If they decide that they want to serve another year, which again is voluntary, they can opt to spend it all with one service or six months each in two different services.

They will not be placed in harm's way unless they specifically request combat duty, which depending on their level of training may in certain circumstances be granted, although not as front-line combatants.

Free university accommodation and food

In return for this second year's service, they will, in addition to free university fees, receive free accommodation while at the university and a generous food and clothing allowance, which only excludes alcohol and condom purchases. (Hang on a minute, I might actually instruct the Education Department to cover those condoms before I leave, now that I'm reminded.)

Predictably, at first students recoiled in horror at the idea of national service, but after the first batch of volunteers were encouraged to openly share their daily experiences on social media, the sight of their friends having so many free opportunities and such great fun at government expense caused 78 per cent of the rest of that gap year to volunteer immediately.

68 per cent of the first-year draft also volunteered for second-year duty – far more than anticipated.

The result of this programme is that the majority of the next generation of university graduates will have more self-discipline and better life skills, and they will be a lot less whiny and self-centred than their predecessors, leading them to become better and more useful citizens.

The programme has also led to the largest increase in TA recruit-ment in history as a significant proportion of students, about 24 per cent, have joined up while at university, not only doing their bit for the country but getting well paid for it as well.

Free university education for voluntary national service worked like a dream, GTJD.

Rehabilitation centres for human-trafficking victims

The highly successful Gang Busters operation by the SMOG led to the rounding up of a large number of people-trafficking victims. Most of the attractive Eastern European girls had been forced to work as prostitutes.

Anticipating that this would be the case, I had ordered my team to find couple of bankrupt boarding schools in rural locations, purchase them and then convert them into secure institutions by constructing a large wire fence around them and installing security posts at the entrances.

All existing sports facilities like swimming pools, tennis courts and playing fields were repaired and upgraded and the interiors were redecorated in pleasant contemporary colour schemes and furnished with comfortable furniture and nice curtains.

The dormitories and studies were converted into bedrooms, mostly designed to be shared by no more than two girls. Bedroom doors were not to be locked and there was a high ratio of bathrooms to bedrooms, no less than one to every two rooms.

Hallways were nicely carpeted and, when completed, the two locations resembled five-star hotels rather than the temporary secure institutions that they actually were.

When the people-trafficking victims, or PTVs, were first brought to these two institutions they were usually in a terrible physical and a fragile mental state. Most had been forced to become dependent on drugs and were terrified of what would now happen to them.

Firstly, a medical team ran comprehensive tests to determine if they had any sexual transmitted diseases or other medical problems, along with a toxicity check to determine what chemicals they had in their systems. They then received treatment for all of these problems in the well-equipped and expertly staffed sanatoriums.

Once cleared of any infections, the next step was to start the long road to building up their self-esteem and confidence.

This has always presented a challenge when dealing with traumatised people. When the Allied forces liberated the concentration camps towards the end of World War II, psychologists were employed to try and find the best way of restoring morale and self-esteem to the inmates. Food and medicine helped the body, but the mind was something else, actually a greater challenge after people had been exposed to so much horror.

They found that the single most important thing that they could give women to restore their will to survive was the simplest and cheapest item, something that meant more to them than even food: lipstick.

Any female concentration-camp victim will testify that the day the parachute supply bags turned up with little sticks of lipstick was the day they started to feel like human beings again.

We were in the fortunate position to offer far more than just lipstick to these poor girls. Once out of the sanatorium, they were then supplied with a completely new wardrobe of smart, fashion-able upmarket clothes, bought by the programme or donated by a supportive and generous public. Then, having received attention from hairdressers, beauticians and manicurists, they were shown their bedrooms and taken for a tour of the comprehensive facilities.

At this stage all of the PTVs were being chemically treated for their drug addiction and given special medication twice a day to ward off the terrifying effects of cold turkey. Over the next twelve months the carefully monitored dosages were reduced until in the final stages they were consuming placebos. After a month of taking these with no side effects, they were informed that they were completely cured.

On their day of arrival it was explained to the PTVs that for the sake of their own well-being they would remain in the secure institution until they were completely weaned off narcotics and healthy again.

Most were pathetically grateful to be safe and away from their captors and in a supportive, caring and exceptionally pleasant environment. All of them assured us that they would not consider making any attempt to escape.

They were encouraged to give contact details for their parents who were then flown over free of charge and allowed to stay in the visitors' wing for two weeks at a time.

Many of the parents understandably wanted their daughters to return straight away with them. However, it was explained to them that their child would only be free to leave once they were completely off drugs and totally rehabilitated.

It was further explained to them, that the girls were receiving English lessons and also studying in a special British citizenship education programme. If they passed with high enough marks they would be offered the chance of British citizenship and could then legally stay in Britain.

Nearly 40 per cent of the PTVs, many of whom were very bright, passed and have stayed, hopefully to become happy productive citizens. The others returned to their homes abroad, but at least every single one of them was given her life back.

I made an incognito visit to both the PTV rehab centres towards the end of the programme and it was a heart-warming experience to see all the tanned, healthy, happy, smiling inmates laughing and shrieking while they ran around playing tennis and hockey and generally acting like they were just normal university girls from nice homes rather than the survivors of a living hell.

This programme, operated without regard to expense, cost tens of millions. This was not a problem because every penny came from the cash and sale of the assets seized by the SMOG from the crime lords before they went on their nice little cruise.

Rehabilitating the PTV, putting the proceeds of evil to good use for once, GTJD.

Chapter nine

Identity Theft

Identity theft is such a serious problem in Britain that I set aside some time to combat it directly.

Here is the thing: before I took over, every official document a citizen possessed – their driving licence, identity card, student card, shotgun certificate, NHS card and so on – openly displayed *three* vital pieces of information that every identity thief required. Their *address*, their *place* of birth and *date* of birth were printed bold as brass for the identity thieves to use.

Only the address was left off their passports but the other two vital items, *place and date of birth* were there for all to see.

It is an accepted fact that a great deal of identity theft, or IT, takes place during everyday transactions. Let's say a teenager shows their driving licence at an off licence in order to buy alcohol. All the person on the till has to do is remember or scribble down the four salient details, name, address, date of birth and place of birth and they can use that information to do anything.

I have brought this ridiculous situation to an end using the simplest common-sense measure imaginable, a programme I called No Vital Info, or NVI.

NVI

Under NVI, all new passports, driving licences and other official documents have the vital information concerning date and place of birth, and in the case of driving licences, their home addresses, removed from open view. All such information is stored on the documents' electronic chip only.

Passports

Every passport control in the world scans passports electronically and can read the person's date and place of birth off the electronic chip. So having it on display is pointless.

Now this vital information is no longer on show, all the passport control officers need to do is discretely ask each passport holder for these details to determine whether it is theirs or has been stolen. As people always have to approach the passport control individually, there is no chance of an identity thief overhearing the answers.

Not 100 per cent foolproof maybe, but this simple measure does, however, increase passport security several thousand per cent for the princely sum of, err, nothing. That's right, not a single penny, in fact it saves money because there are two fewer lines to print than on an old-style passport.

Driving licences

With these, for added security, the address lines can be deleted as well as date of birth and place of birth. All traffic police check the identity of any driver they stop on the laptops in their patrol cars now, so why have any vital information on display? Again it is the perfect opportunity for a policeman to check if the licence has been stolen and modified.

Foot patrols always radio into their HQ to confirm identity too, so again all they need to do is read the driving licence number over their radios and then ask the individual to confirm the details.

If they don't know their own date and place of birth and home address, clearly they are using a stolen identity. *Duh*.

Off licences, bars and nightclubs – green or red reader

It is now a requirement under the licensing act for every licensed premises and off licence to have a simple driving-licence/identity-card-reading machine that does *not* reveal the age or place of birth to the operator but simply calculates if the person is older or younger than eighteen and turns green or red accordingly.

The Internet

I passed laws making it illegal for market research organisations or utility companies such as electricity suppliers to obtain date and place of birth. This includes all social media platforms and credit card-processing companies. It is now a level 5 crime to attempt to obtain these vital details from any British citizen.

The NVI programme and the Internet law changes have reduced identity theft in Britain by 92 per cent and so proved very successful.

The only problem encountered as a result of the NVI programme was that for the first nine months, the Passport Office and the DVLA were swamped with nearly seventeen million requests for replacement passports and driving licenses, many from ladies of a certain age, who had mysteriously 'lost' their existing ones simultaneously.

I had anticipated this situation, however, and before making the change to the passports and driving licences, I temporarily trebled the staff at these offices and streamlined the production processes, while at the same time I raised the replacement cost for 'lost' documents to £150 for passports and £70 for driving licences, thus raising well over £3.5 billion in clear net revenue after the extra printing and staffing costs.

The vanity element played right into my hands as not only did it raise revenue but it also converted seventeen million current passports and driving licences right away, which would otherwise have been converted only at their expiry dates.

NVI virtually eliminated identity theft *and* made a massive amount of wonga for the Treasury in the process. GTJD.

Chapter ten

Health and Fitness

Because I am a dictator, I don't have to be politically correct. I have the luxury of doing what no politician is able to do, and that is speak the truth. In regard to health and fitness in Britain, the shameful truth is very simple.

The British population is not fit enough and the vast majority of them are too fat.

When I was at school, there was always one, possibly two, fat kids, at the very most, in the class. Before I took over, if I walked into a classroom, it was the other way around. I would be lucky to see more than one or two kids of the correct weight for their height and age.

Well, you know what? To hell with that nonsense! From the day I took over, this utterly unacceptable situation, which was entirely the fault of the PCB, started on the long road to reversal.

It is possible to accept that a very small proportion of overweight children are that way due to genetics, but 90 per cent of them? I am sorry, not on your life. That's the result of quite *avoidable* bad diet and *lack of exercise*.

I realised that obesity in the school population was a bombshell waiting to explode on the NHS in years to come. Illnesses due to obesity in the overweight parents and even grandparents was already making a massive impact on NHS resources and if it had been allowed to continue at the current rate it would have become the single largest expense for this country.

Overstretched NHS

Logistically, my expert number crunchers calculated that even with our newly doubled budget, it would have been impossible to maintain a large enough NHS to cope with the sheer volume of heart conditions, diabetes and other diseases brought about by the ludicrously irresponsible attitude of schools in no longer insisting on compulsory exercise, and of parents to their children's diet.

Good thing I came along when I did then; otherwise Britain would have been in serious trouble.

It was quite clear how this situation has come about. Bad diet, food additives and fast food have obviously had a devastating impact, but the other main cause is that games are no longer compulsory. I mean, for God's sake, most of the school playing fields had been sold off for development. How crazy is that?

When I was in school, all the way from seven to eighteen years old we played two hours of compulsory sport per day and compulsorily attended two full-on hard PT sessions per week, each of which lasted two hours.

The impact of this lasts a lifetime. When I look at any of my school friends, now in their late forties, the vast majority of them are still fit. A little bit of middle-aged spread here and there aside, they are still in massively better shape than the rest of the population and suffer far fewer serious health problems.

Most of my friends still play some kind of sport or indulge in hard physical activity regularly, and sadly for those with children in state schools, most of them are still a lot fitter than their own kids, who are less than half their age.

All right, so this how I set about quite literally saving the population of Britain from ending up like the monster-sized Americans, where 300 lb-plus men and 200 lb-plus women with thighs the size of a normal man's waist are commonplace.

I called the programme appropriately, Fat Busting.

Fat Busting

First a change of attitude was required. All the PCB nonsense protecting the concept of people being overweight (and therefore allowing it to be regarded as normal, which is what has happened in the USA) was outlawed. Now, by law it is fine to call overweight kids and adults what they actually are – *fat*. Pretty soon, children in particular no longer felt complacent about it.

If this hurt a few people's feelings, well tough; better to lose weight in order to avoid embarrassment at ten years old than find yourself in hospital getting a double heart bypass at forty-five.

My PR gurus studied what motivated schoolchildren and created a programme to persuade pupils that being fat is not cool any longer; in fact it is as uncool as it gets.

'How many of your favourite celebrities are fat?' This was the question put to them. 'Do you think that these people became that cool and sexy by sitting on their fat bums all day scoffing fast food? NO. So why would you want to ruin your body doing just that? You can turn yourself into a cool person too by exercising like they obviously do (to get a butt like Soap Opera Sharon has, or abs like Daytime TV Darren has, or whatever) and then if you are careful about what you eat, maybe then you will end up on TV too.'

To a generation brought up on reality TV shows full of brainless banal people whose only attributes are their looks and bodies, that sort of approach has some effect. Anything to motivate them is fine by me. Honestly, I will go to any lengths to GTJD.

I passed a law making it compulsory for schools to provide two hours' sport a day and four hours of PT per week, with no exceptions. In my day the fat kids who were naturally overweight, genetically, had to do exactly the same exercise as the rest of us and by the time they had reached their teens, they were a darn sight slimmer than they would have been otherwise, and most importantly, as least as fit as the rest of us if not even more so because they had to work harder at it.

I served with guys in the Royal Marines, and believe it or not, even the SBS, who would have been fat naturally if they had just allowed it to happen, but guess what? They didn't, but instead became real-life superheroes.

I have made certain that every school in the land has access to playing fields and sports facilities. In some cases this meant the compulsory purchase of the original playing fields and even the reverse development of some locations to their original state.

Under Fat Busting, all schoolchildren were compulsorily weighed throughout the land and in the vast majority of cases the parents were brought in and told in plain English that their kids were too fat and that was going to be reversed whether they liked it or not.

The parents were given dietary advice and informed about a compulsory daily exercise programme for their child that would be happening at school.

In regard to diet they were given quarterly targets to achieve. If their child did not meet these then they would be fined £250 for every quarter that they missed the target weight. Refusal to participate became a level 1 crime subject to Double Up. These policies focused their attention, I can tell you.

One other major contributory factor to fatness today for school children is that due to modern traffic conditions very few of them can walk or cycle to school. Realistically this cannot be changed, on safety grounds, and I would never suggest doing so. However, what can be changed are the school buses themselves.

Exercise buses

When I was touring America one year on my Triumph Tiger 800 motorbike, I visited Nashville in Tennessee and I was amused to see that they had mobile bars travelling around the city. These were propelled by the drinkers at the bar who were pedalling them while a member of staff, who presumably remains sober, steered. The natural competitiveness of the human spirit led to impromptu races between rival mobile bars and everyone gained fitness as they enjoyed getting pissed.

This gave me an idea. With so much concern for the environment and the pressure for public transport to be switched to electric hybrid vehicles, why not combine the two areas of pollution-reduction with the pressing need for children to take more exercise?

I had my engineering department design a new hybrid electric school bus, which relied on every child pedalling to constantly charge the recycled-ex-HGV batteries we installed in them. Please don't misunderstand me – not to *propel* the bus, just to *charge* the batteries. This has proved to be a perfectly practical idea.

We found that twenty to forty children were capable of creating more than enough energy to ensure the batteries remain charged. In doing so not only are they able to replace the exercise they were losing out on by no longer walking or cycling to school, but they also gain a sense of achievement and participation in transporting themselves.

At a time when everyone takes so much for granted, this opportunity to contribute to their transportation to and from school helps them develop a sense of responsibility about using resources to travel.

There is also another factor. Today there is so little sense of adventure in being a schoolchild. When everyone rode a bicycle to school there were always all sorts of mini adventures along the way. Perhaps, for instance, you would see a rare sight like a family of stoats crossing the road in front of you or find an adjustable spanner or some other treasure, which had fallen out of a vehicle.

Maybe you would stumble across the girl you fancied in year 5 stranded on the road with a puncture, and you would have the opportunity to become her instant hero by fixing it and this would lead to snogging her behind the bike shed later. Anything could happen when you were master of your own transportation. When you set off in the morning you never knew what would happen.

Until our new electric pedal-charged buses hit the streets all that everyday real-life adventure had gone for kids. Instead they were used to simply getting on a bus, travelling to school and then getting off. No wonder they were resorting to living fantasy existences through video games.

Now however, none of these children will ever forget the adventures they had 'pedalling' their bus to school. It will prove an inspiring memory for the rest of their lives and help them develop a lateral-thinking approach to life and stimulate the inventive British spirit that has led to us filing more significant patents than any other country in the world.

The new bus has a very small conventional diesel engine as a back-up charging unit rather than for propulsion, but this is normally only used to top up the batteries should they run low on the way back to the depot after the children have been dropped off.

Due to brilliant design on behalf of my team, the gearing on the pedals is such that every child gets almost the same exercise riding to school on the new exercise buses that they would on a normal cycle, while at the same time doing their bit to reduce pollution in the local environment.

The pedalling effort is not arduous by any means, but it is consistent exercise, which is equivalent to a child pedalling a normal bicycle on a flat road at 15 m.p.h. On hills an inclinometer in the control unit ensures that an appropriate and modest amount of extra effort is required by the pupils.

This extra effort is not actually *required* by the buses' charging system to go up hill; it is there purely in the interests of realism and to encourage a sense of participation.

If the pupils want to increase the speed by pedalling faster, they can ask the driver to switch to Input Mode, and if road conditions allow it, the driver can then flick a switch that links their combined pedal output to speed. Again, the increase in effort is not directly linked to the propulsion system, but it is detected by the power-control unit and interpreted as a request for more speed in the same way as pressing the accelerator.

The driver can of course override this at any time by applying the brakes or accelerator, for reasons of safety.

If conditions allow, in Input Mode the pupils in one bus can race another bus. If the rivalry created results in fitter pupils, that's all good.

Each pupil's bus seat has a detector unit on it, so any child attempting to get away with not pedalling can be punished by extra PT instead of lunch when they get to school.

In cases in which a school did not have its own playing fields, the pupils get the benefit of extra exercise on the way to one of the many new out-of-town playing fields that I have created through compulsory development.

Electric exercise train carriages

Following the success of the school exercise buses, I thought it would be a good idea to extend this to trains. Now a certain proportion of all trains have exercise carriages in which people can pedal down the cost of their fare by generating electricity if they wish, thus saving the diesel required by the train to generate it. The exercise seats have a swipe reader for tickets. Once swiped, these units display the cost of the ticket and deduct energy credit from that cost as the passenger pedals.

At the end of the journey the passenger can retrieve a refund from special machines installed in the station, which top up their credit or debit card with the relevant amount.

All long-distance and commuter trains also have at least one bicycle carriage where keen cyclists can mount their bikes on fixed stands with roller-based electricity generators and pedal as hard as they like. Some really fit cyclists not only pedal the cost of their ticket down to zero but can also accumulate further discounts for future travel on an Oyster-type rail-fare card.

Fast food chains

I passed laws banning virtually everything sold in the American fast-food chains. They could remain in business in the UK only on the strict proviso that they served approved menus consisting of healthy food with no added preservatives or chemicals.

Some chains complied and actually created some very appetising healthy fast food. Other companies simply packed up and left. Excellent! Bloody good riddance to them.

Supermarkets

These were issued with stringent new directives concerning the food they could sell. All fat-causing ingredients and preservatives were banned completely. This made certain ready-made meals unviable but that was no loss.

By necessity it also shortened the supply chain, so supermarkets were forced to buy fresh produce from local suppliers, and therefore they were forced to pay a higher price and support local farmers more. However, a new law prevented them from passing more than half this extra cost to the consumer.

On the other hand, the transport costs for the supermarkets fell considerably as the local farmers did the delivering, so actually it affected their profit margins less than they anticipated. Pity that had never occurred to them before.

These measures predictably led to a small increase in the cost of food, which on average increased by 2 per cent. However, now that more than 80 per cent of the population no longer pay tax, this is not a problem.

Sweets and crisps and fizzy drinks

Sweets, crisps and fizzy drinks containing high quantities of sugar can only be sold to people over eighteen who show ID, in the same way as alcohol is subject to the same penalties. This new legislation, although far from totally foolproof, is a measure that at least helps parents control their children's intake and meet the quarterly weight targets.

Fat gene elimination

I have put the top geneticists in the land on the task of identifying how to eliminate the fat gene and I have given them a budget you could launch a space mission with. Once this has been done, all couples with one or both fat partners will be compulsorily treated before they are allowed to produce children.

Eugenics? Certainly, but ask yourself how it is that before the two world wars there was no obesity in Britain at all. Sending all the tallest, fittest young men to die, mostly as virgins in the case of the first war, while leaving the fat unfit ones at home to breed, was an exercise in negative eugenics if ever there was one.

In contrast, the Zulu race, which is notably still tall, slim and strong to this day, never allowed a young man to join the ranks of the impi and go to war before fathering a child. Furthermore, they didn't allow any of the young men to breed unless they *had* passed all the arduous physical tests to become a warrior and join the impi in the first place, so that eliminated all their inferior gene stock.

This was a nation that in Victorian times we used to call primitive savages. Well, they call us the white hippos, so who's laughing now?

Time to get real

I'm sorry but it was time to get real; our population simply could not have sustained the continuous increase in totally *avoidable* fatness foisted on us by the PCB. Someone had to sweep aside all their namby-pamby nonsense and take control of the situation.

Fat Busting, obviously not an instant result, but slowly but surely it is working. GTJD.

The new NHS, now the best in the world

The first thing I did was to allocate all of the £87.6 billion saved annually by sending the criminals on their nice little cruise to fund a massive NHS expansion and improvement programme and allocate this same sum every year to double its current annual budget. However, before I allowed a single penny to be spent, I did something else first: I put the Dutch in charge of it.

I put the Irish in charge of saving the English language because, in my opinion, they were the best-qualified race in the world to do the job. By the same token, if I was to turn the existing National Health Service around and reinvent it as the best health service in the world, I knew I had to get the best-qualified people to come in and sort it out, and in the case of health care, that is the clog cloppers.

To put it in perspective, year in, year out the Netherlands has taken pole position as the best health service in Europe. We on the other hand scored fourteenth place, just ahead of Romania, where the concept of anaesthetisation consists of a heavy wooden mallet.

I sacked everybody currently involved in running the NHS and replaced all senior management and, wherever possible, middle management positions with highly qualified Dutch managers. My brief to them was to completely change the culture within the NHS to the way things are done in the Netherlands, and if they encountered too much resistance, to get their section chiefs to call me personally.

Not only did I put the Dutch in charge of running the NHS, I also engaged the best German hospital builders to build brand-new hospitals throughout the land. These were designed by our finest British architects, and based on the very best examples from anywhere in the world.

Because the Germans would be building them, I knew from experience that they would be constructed in half the time that it would take anyone else and that everything would work when it was turned on for the first time.

I swept aside all planning red tape and ordered the hospitals to be built in the optimum locations to serve the local communities based on common sense and need rather than petty planning regulations. In a number of cases, where the redundant local prison was situated within city limits and could provide the local population with a conveniently located new hospital, we were able to redevelop the sites of these unoccupied buildings.

One of my conditions for allocating the building contracts to the German firms was that they employed a certain proportion of British building workers at all levels of skill and ensured that they were trained to do things the German way.

The German building culture is typified by all of the respective trades, such as electricians, plumbers, carpenters and so forth, helping each other and working together as one big friendly team to improve efficiency, rather than getting in each other's way and acting as rivals, which unfortunately has always been the traditional way here.

I thought the massive new hospital-building programme would be a good opportunity to start changing our current construction culture by exposing lots of young British apprentices to the more efficient and holistic German approach.

Once these flagship hospitals were built, there would never be a shortage of doctors, specialists or highly trained nurses to staff them, thanks to my deal with Cuba.

So the best and most efficient National Health Service in the entire world. Funded by getting rid of the criminals, run by the Dutch, designed by the British, built by the Germans and staffed by the Cubans, GTJD.

Chapter eleven

Banks and Hedge Funds

It is 2005 and I am standing outside a cocktail bar in Sloane Square on a warm summer evening having an idle chat with some irritatingly smug git working in a hedge fund with whom I have fallen into casual conversation. As everyone I have ever met working in hedge funds is called Giles, let's call him that. Giles was explaining to me in his arrogant, loud, braying way how he had recently purchased a briefcase full of toxic debt called something like a CDO or CDS or some other meaningless acronym.

He tells me that some chap from one of the major banks walked into his office the week before with this briefcase and told him that although it was valued at £100 million, his boss wanted to sell it at a discount, for £90 million. Giles apparently then asked the bank bod what was in it and he replied that he believed it was a cross section of good and sub-prime mortgages or credit swaps or defaults or something – actually, he didn't really know, and even if he did, he would no more have understood it than Giles would have.

But hey, the important thing was that *whatever* it was in the briefcase, it had a triple-A rating and paid 18 per cent return, in other words 18 million a year.

Hello? A what? A triple-A rating?

A triple-A rating is granted to the kind of investment that is so safe that you buy it for your granny to cover her retirement-home costs. In a market paying 6 per cent on your high-street savings, you expect a triple A to pay 4 per cent at best, but you buy it because you know a triple-A rating means that Britain would disappear under 20 ft of ice before your granny could ever lose her money. That is why it is called triple A.

I point out to Giles the impossibility of a financial implement paying 18 per cent in a market that was paying 6 per cent on the high street while at the same time carrying a triple-A rating.

Giles guffaws loudly while nodding vigorously like a drunk donkey and then goes on to explain why he bought it, and in so doing he also explained, without realising it himself, exactly how the financial meltdown of 2007 came to pass.

As he started to gob off in his annoying braying way, a cold shiver passed down my spine. I knew with absolute certainty as I listened to this arrogant little twat that we were standing on the edge of disaster and all of us were totally buggered.

Giles snorts 'Oh yaaah, of course I knew it was a total bag of shite, but why should I care? As long as some rating agency has given it a triple-A rating, then due-diligence wise, that clears me to buy it on behalf of the fund. The way my bonus scheme works on something paying 18 per cent, I pick up 2 per cent, which is obviously £2 million a year for every year it pays out, so if it only lasts two to three years before going pop, well that's £4 or £6 million for doing no more than scribbling my signature on the contract. It hasn't cost me a penny, after all. It's the fund's money buying it. There is no risk to me, so what do I care?'

I thought, *'That's right Giles, you disgusting, greedy little scumbag. What do you care?'*

I loathe greedy bankers and hedge funders like Sloane Square Giles so much that when I first came to power I seriously considered ordering the SMOG to round the whole lot up and send them on the same cruise as the criminals, which after all is what a lot of them really are anyway.

Tempting though it was, it would have destroyed Britain's financial standing, so it was off the cards. However, I have been able to clip their wings considerably.

The politicians before me had made a great play of doing just that, but predictably it was just a phoney half-hearted attempt. Far too many of their own children, and indeed their mates, were riding the gravy train in the City to really do anything significant. Plus, when top politicians retire now they get lucrative directorships in the City, so they are not going to screw up their retirement plans, that's for sure.

Has it ever occurred to you to ask yourself why the banks offer top politicians million-pound retirement packages for attending a nice lunch once a quarter as a so-called non-executive director? It is totally obvious when you think about it. They do it to ensure that the politicians don't rock the boat when they are in power.

Think it through logically and you will realise I am right, because as these 'politicians' are not licensed bankers, they couldn't possibly act as real non-executive directors in any capacity in such a closely regulated industry.

Anyway, one of the benefits of being a dictator is that I don't have to give a damn about anything like that, so I just go ahead and do the right thing.

One of the last lot of politicians made a big deal out of limiting bonus schemes. That was just a smokescreen to pacify a gullible public. It would never work, and frankly if it did, all it would do is ensure the brightest people from the City went to America or somewhere else.

No, only a fool tries to interfere with market forces. What was required was something with more teeth.

What I did sent shock waves through everyone in the banking sector. I swiftly passed some new laws specifically addressing the issue of banker and hedge fund greed.

First I repealed all previous legislation restricting bonus levels, because I knew the top people would find a way of hiding their true earnings anyway, so leaving the legislation in place would only create more barriers to discovering the true figures and the whereabouts of the cash.

The jubilation in the City on hearing this news was short lived when they read about another a new programme called Clawback. It works like this.

Clawback

When, not *if*, but *when* the next financial meltdown comes along as a result of selfish, irresponsible, greedy activity of bankers and hedge funders, now *every single* person involved in the decision-making chain, irrespective of how small or great their standing in society, has their bank accounts and assets frozen.

Then forensic accountants in my newly formed Financially Unlimited Clawback Unit, or the appropriately abbreviated FUCU, calculate how much the people involved personally earned from the scam they started, including all earnings and bonuses from the day they first signed it off. Then an allowance for all recorded tax paid and a living allowance of £50,000 per annum is deducted. Once this bill has been calculated, they are then given twelve months to pay.

Meanwhile all their assets are frozen, except for the purposes of selling them to pay the fine, and their passports seized. They are allowed to leave the country on bona-fide business trips or to assist in the recovery of overseas cash or assets but only under the escort of three armed members of the SMOG. They are not allowed to leave the country with their families or while their families are abroad.

For every million they are short, they serve one year in jail. If they owe £36 million and have so far only raised £20 million by the end of the twelve-month period, they go to jail for sixteen years but can buy a year off their sentence for every million they continue to raise by selling assets or 'remembering' where they stashed their offshore money, until the remaining debt is paid in cash or years.

A change in the law now means that assets and cash transferred to wives or other family members is fully recoverable and subject to Clawback.

To ensure that there is a sufficient motivation to 'pay rather than stay', financial criminals, or FCs as they are called, are exclusively sent to Dartmoor. As Britain has very few criminals now, Dartmoor is one of the few remaining prisons that has not been redeveloped into a hospital, hotel, spa or apartment block because it is too grim for anyone to want to redevelop it.

Apart from the hospital redevelopments, this sell-off programme of prisons raised billions for the Treasury incidentally.

Dartmoor FC prisoners are required to spend six days a week breaking granite rocks with sledgehammers from dawn till dusk, no matter what the weather, which is foul for most of the time. Trust me I know, having frozen my butt off while training on the moor in the Royal Marines.

Ratings agencies

Some of the ratings agencies have a great deal to answer for. How these organisations get way with allocating triple-A ratings to worthless, flawed financial instruments time after time, boom and bust after boom and bust, defies belief. Every time a financial bubble bursts it turns out to be many of the same ratings companies who have helped it to dangerously inflate in the first place with these criminally irresponsible ratings.

Back at the turn of the twenty-first century, at the millennium, it was some of the very same agencies that allocated triple-A ratings to worthless dot-com companies, most of which were pure fantasy investments and then went on to allocate triple-A ratings to in the last sub-prime CDO-type scams, thus allowing the likes of Sloane Square Giles to make fortunes.

Do you think they allocated these ridiculous ratings for bona-fide reasons or because somewhere along the line they had a nice little payday?

Think about it: a child could work out that 18 per cent and a triple-A rating is an impossible match in a 6 per cent return market.

Why the politicians sat on their hands and allow it to openly happen right in front of them is a question that haunts me. It just proves that the whole lot of them were either too corrupt or too gutless to run a country. That's why I had to step in.

To deal with these irresponsible, if not outright criminal, organisations once and for all I passed some new legislation. Any ratings agency which allocates triple-A or similar ratings to a financial scam, which subsequently goes bust causing untold misery to ordinary people in society, is now held accountable.

Firstly all board members are charged as FCs and fined a

minimum of £10 million apiece, which they either pay off or work off in years by breaking rocks on Dartmoor.

Secondly, all FCs actually responsible for signing off bogus triple-A ratings serve a minimum of an extra fifteen years on Dartmoor in addition to the £10 million or whatever fraction of that they can pay to reduce the primary ten-year sentence.

If this means some have to spend up to twenty-five years breaking rocks on Dartmoor, so be it.

I have no pity for some of these phoney ratings agency people. Just like Sloane Square Giles, in my view they are some of the worst parasitic criminals in society and they are lucky not to be at the bottom of the Atlantic where they belong.

There is now nowhere on earth an FC can hide. If they scoot abroad and extradition orders cannot be obtained, I will simply send in the SMOG to capture them and bring them home with overwhelming speed and efficiency, body-bagging bodyguards as they do so, if necessary. For every day an FC has hidden abroad, an extra million is added to their bill.

Once the Clawback measures came into force, one could see a lot of very worried people shuffling around in the City with long ashen faces wondering when the axe was going to fall on them, and suddenly there was a lot less loud arrogant braying in the City bars.

The market value of exotic cars like Rolls Royce, Porsche and Lamborghinis in London collapsed as the guilty offloaded them and other visible trappings of wealth in an effort to lower their profile. They might as well have kept them. Nothing will save them from the FUCU and the SMOG when their activities come to light.

Clawback has certainly made its presence felt. There is now no enthusiasm whatsoever for ratings agencies to allocate bogus ratings to worthless financial scams and for banks and hedge funds to become involved in deliberately creating future bubbles in order to make a quick buck.

Clawback certainly stopped the gravy train dead in its tracks and GTJD.

High Street Banks

I passed a law requiring every high street bank to have two things.

First of these is that every bank branch must have its own separate telephone number so customers can speak directly to the staff on duty.

Secondly, every branch must also have at least one experienced bank manager with a minimum of fifteen years' experience in banking to deal with customers' enquiries and problems.

Failure to comply with either of these requirements results in a fine of £10,000 per day per branch.

Financial Advisors

There is no such thing as a financial advisor; they are all financial products salesmen and now that is all they are allowed to call themselves or they face a £100,000 fine for the first offence and one year in jail for the second, subject to Double Up.

Chapter twelve

Employment

I am not one who subscribes to the theory that all the long-term unemployed are work-shy freeloaders. I believe that many would love to work but for a combination of reasons cannot get a break to prove themselves.

Many of the long-term unemployed live in rundown areas with very limited employment opportunities. Some of these areas have been created by the policies of previous administrations. The destruction of the coal mining industry is a good example.

Take the example of a northern mining town in the 1980s with 100 per cent employment and a highly developed social infra-structure, which traditionally looked after its own extended families and possessed too much pride to allow their elderly or sick to rely on benefits.

One day the mines are closed and so it suddenly has its source of income completely removed. With no other industry in the area, this once-strong and proud community gradually turns into the exact opposite. Crime inevitably takes over the role of employment for the next generation, hence gang culture thrives and drugs become a way of life.

I have great sympathy for many of these areas, but I realised that what was needed to turn all this around were some robust and drastic measures, the sort of measures that would undoubtedly horrify the PCB loony liberal types. But then as a dictator, I don't mind what they harp on about. I called the programme simply Work Training.

Work Training

Firstly, I ordered my property team, the same team that purchased the bankrupt boarding schools for the PTV rehab programme, to find surplus military camps with plenty of land around them. Next I had them staff these camps with qualified trade trainers capable of teaching specific trades covering everything from bricklaying right through to basic vehicle maintenance or computer programming, and purchase all necessary plant and equipment to teach the trades concerned.

Special facilities were created for the disabled in one particular camp and appropriate, relevant instructors appointed for them.

Enviably, as these military camps had been around since the 1940s, some accommodation buildings were in a better state of repair than others, ranging from leaking, draughty Nissen huts right through to modern centrally heated blocks. This suited my purposes very well and I instructed the property team not to improve the worst buildings but to leave then just as they were and concentrate on bringing the better buildings up to a very comfortable standard.

All of the long-term unemployed were then ordered, in drafts of 250 at a time, to a central aptitude assessment centre, or AAC, near Norwich. Any who did not turn up were rounded up by the police and informed that they either attend or face two years in jail, as failure to report had become a level 2 crime.

The sexes were drafted separately to avoid complications; they would also be sent to separate institutions for the duration of the training period. The whole programme was already going to be challenging enough for the instructors as it was without the draftees shagging each other as well.

The draftees were then interviewed at the AAC and set a series of compulsory aptitude and physiological tests. They were also asked if there was any particular trade or occupation that they aspired to.

Having completed all the tests they were taken to various parts of the centre's extensive grounds and over the next five days given the chance of having a go at a wide range of activities based on trade craft, ranging from soldering a plumbing joint right through to computer programming. At the end of this week, they were interviewed again and asked if there was any particular trade that interested them. Usually more than half had a firm opinion and others were still not sure.

Based on their performance in their week at the AAC, the draftees were transported to the most appropriate work training centres on the former military camps around the country.

At these centres the draftees were split into two groups. Those who had displayed enthusiasm for learning a particular trade or indeed simply a general enthusiasm for the programme itself and the chance to turn their lives around were sent to the modern comfortable buildings. This group was unofficially referred to by the trainers among themselves as the Positives. Usually more than 60 per cent of the draft fell into this category.

Not only were these buildings comfortable but they were also equipped with big screen TVs and games like table football and table tennis.

The second group, known confidentially to the trainers as the Negatives, consisted of people who appeared indifferent to the training and otherwise displayed a bad attitude. They were billeted in the oldest, coldest, leakiest Nissen huts with very basic toilet and shower facilities, with no games and only a small old-fashioned TV.

After a week or so, the Negative group were given a tour of the nicer accommodation enjoyed by the Positive group and it was then explained to them that all they needed to do to move to better accommodation like the others was to get their act together and become involved with the programme.

I knew from personal experience that cold damp Nissen huts would be a strong motivator for the less enthusiastic to improve their lot. I have lain awake at night freezing and sneezing in enough of them on Dartmoor while in the military.

There was also another motivating factor: once the good trainees passed their basic test, they received the minimum wage whereas those who couldn't be bothered stayed on benefits.

The vast majority of the Positive trainees progressed swiftly through their training and once they had passed the first of their basic tests were allowed off the camp at weekends. The Negative ones were not allowed to go anywhere, but their ranks were thinning every day as gradually the benefits of learning a trade or simply displaying a better attitude to the programme and a willingness to work resulted in a progressive promotion from the worst accommodation to warmer Nissen huts with better facilities and ultimately to the modern accommodation.

Much of the belligerence and bravado displayed by members of the Negative group was simply hiding a lack of self-confidence; many of them had given up on themselves and on life in general. Our psychologists had devised methods of addressing this. One ruse to boost self-esteem was for an instructor to pretend he had a problem and confide in a particular Negative trainee and so display trust and faith in him to help him out.

For instance, the instructor would pretend that some idiot delivery driver had dumped some pallets of breeze blocks in the wrong area and he was going to get in trouble with his boss unless it was moved, but it had to done quickly and on the quiet. He would ask a recalcitrant Negative group member if he or she could help him out.

Many of the Negative group had never experienced anyone putting trust in them, or if it had happened it was too long ago to count. Subtle little tricks like this combined with a generally supportive atmosphere, based around small but achievable weekly goals, gradually brought the majority of them around.

It was highly significant that once the attitude change came about, they then progressed rapidly through the training and started to catch up with the Positive group.

Usually, by the end of the first month the vast majority of the Negative group were living in the modern accommodation and displaying a much more positive attitude to learning a trade and to work and life in general.

It is a fact of life that people have different levels of intelligence and aptitude. Half the problem with the PCB is that they try to treat everyone the same for fear of displaying prejudice, but actually end up making the less able feel worthless because they can't deliver.

Our programme allowed people of all abilities to feel they were achieving something and all of them left the programme with a recognised vocational qualification. The brightest qualified high enough in trade foundation courses to be placed on full-time trade apprenticeship schemes, receiving the minimum wage until they qualified.

The less able, however, were still trained in something useful and certificated, whether this was for operating jackhammers or driving dumper trucks and they were now equipped to go to work and to do so with a great deal more self-confidence.

Not one of those leaving the work training camps was abandoned; they were all found real jobs to go to upon leaving – not so hard now because of the massive construction programmes going on around the country thanks to the vast cash surplus created by my various revenue-raising programmes.

The new shipbuilding programme for the Navy alone required a vast amount of dry-dock construction and renovation work on the old dockyards, which had stood idle for decades. This programme swallowed up a significant proportion of those leaving the training institutions.

Work Training – being cruel to be kind. Only a dictator could have got away with it, and of course it worked well. GTJD.

Chapter thirteen

Armed Forces

Things were now going very well. The national debt had been rapidly paid off by the revenues from fracking, the NHS had double its budget thanks to the prison population going on their nice little cruise, and thanks to the common-sense tax system, education, pensions, sport and other important sectors were all being covered by the largest tax revenues ever collected by the Treasury. So with a gigantic cash surplus accumulating, it was now time to turn my attention to defence.

I called a meeting with the chief of staff of each of the Armed Forces and explained that it was my intention to very significantly increase their budgets and, with this in mind, requested them to produce a clear but concise plan for investment in resources based in order of priority but with the minimum of military jargon and in plain English.

After finally hearing the news they had been so eagerly awaiting, they scuttled off post-haste to their HQs sporting massive grins from ear to ear.

Although at this stage I did not tell them this, I had already decided how I was going to distribute the long overdue sensible military budget.

Sensible military budget

The Navy: 50 per cent
The Army: 30 per cent
The RAF: 20 per cent

The Royal Navy

I allocated the Royal Navy half of the entire budget. The First Sea Lord, when serving previously as a vice admiral, had been a seasoned veteran of decades of attempting to extract enough money out of successive governments to buy a fleet of rowing boats. When he saw the figure the Navy was to receive, he passed out with shock and had to be revived on my office floor by paramedics.

The logic behind my thinking is as follows. Britain became Great Britain because we had the largest most powerful navy in the world. It would be quite unrealistic to attempt to do that again, because the super-bankrupt countries like America and China will always have unlimited money to print, at least for the foreseeable future, until one day one or both of them can't print any more and it all melts down and turns into the zombie apocalypse.

However, I firmly believed that it was possible to build the most sophisticated and technically advanced navy on the planet if there was a will to do so. We certainly have never lacked the technical ability. Smaller in size than the big boys for sure, but size isn't everything in mortal combat. An elephant will never step on a porcupine if he comes across one on a path because he knows that to do so means a painful, slow and certain death from an infected foot. So, despite being several thousand times bigger than the tiny creature, the elephant walks cautiously around it.

I wanted to build a small navy so deadly that no matter how powerful a future enemy might be, they would rather sail around it than take it on. It wouldn't make us rulers of the waves again, but it sure as hell would make us a serious force to be reckoned with on the global stage and would make Britain defendable against all comers.

Most important of all, it would give us back our national pride.

So the massive shipbuilding programme started. The new compact vessels are constructed from exotic combinations of materials like alloys and carbon fibre resulting in them being very light, manoeuvrable and extremely fast for their size, indeed some are capable of more than 60 knots. All of them are packed to the brim with firepower systems so advanced they are several generations ahead of the Yanks, Russians, Chinese, Koreans and everyone else.

Included in an impressive high-tech arsenal of fast-firing guns and missile systems, the ships are equipped with directed energy pulse guns or DEPG technology, death-ray weapons in plain English. These are capable of destroying missiles and planes at long range for less than fifty-pence worth of electricity. Might come in handy if times get hard again and the Navy can't afford to waste too many expensive conventional munitions.

All craft incorporate stealth technology and active camouflage systems consisting of hundreds of small CCTV cameras mounted all around the ship, recording the sea around them and then perfectly projecting that composite image onto a micro-thin surface covering the ship. What the cameras record on one side of the vessel is projected on the other side, as if the vessel itself is not there to block the view. This technology, combined with thousands of tiny light-emitting diodes embedded in the same special surface mirroring the ambient background light, make the vessels all but invisible.

These active camouflage systems are not a new science; they have been in existence since the 1990s and were fairly accurately depicted on the vanishing Aston Martin Vanquish used in the Bond film *Die Another Day*. However, there had never been enough money available to implement them. Just another example of brilliant British innovation, which without investment would never have become reality.

I ordered the Navy to build craft so stealthy that when their active camouflage systems are switched on, you could sail within a two hundred metres of them and not even see them, let alone detect them on radar, thermal imaging or satellite, and to build them to move so fast they could literally run rings around a potential enemy.

I also ordered the admirals and department heads to come straight to me if they encountered a blockage or any lack of cooperation from anyone along the way. They were all given my direct line and mobile number. Where resistance was encountered, in every case I used my position as dictator to clear the way for them, whether this took appeals to patriotism or outright threats to send the SMOG around to read their horoscope for them in an interview without coffee.

All those involved, from the admirals to the accountants, were aware from the start of the necessity to get the new Navy well underway before the MPs got back into power.

In case future politicians tried to reverse the situation I passed legislation to protect the military from being downgraded, meaning it would take a change in constitutional law to reverse the process, by which time the current plans would be completed.

I also took the precaution of entrusting the top brass of each service with the actual physical funds, each service arm having its own secret offshore escrow bank accounts with three senior officers as signatories, to make it extremely difficult for the MPs to steal it back. I knew that the character of these men is such that they would quite literally be prepared to lay down their lives before allowing this to happen.

Through sheer hard work, the absolute dedication of everyone involved, from admirals to shipwrights, and old-fashioned bloody minded British willpower, in just two years we have already achieved the near impossible. In what would have taken nine or ten years normally, we have laid the keels of a Navy so deadly that no enemy in the world would ever risk taking us on. It will be operational at sea within two more years and Britain will be secure.

The Army

The Army needed the second largest budget, not because I have anything against the RAF, but because no matter what nonsense politicians come out with, the Army will be fighting on the ground in the Middle East for at least another few hundred years, even thousands of years, maybe in fact for ever. This is now a sad fact of life about our existence on this planet and we have to get used to it. That's religion for you.

The first thing I did with the Army heads of staff was to offer them a deal: they could have a free hand to spend the money I was going to allocate to them in any way they chose, but subject to two conditions.

The first condition was that they scrap the current Army rifle, the outdated piece of junk called the SA80, and replace it with the Heckler & Koch HK416, the best-designed and most reliable assault rifle on the planet, which uses the same 5.56 mm ammunition and magazines as the SA80. I further insisted that the best shot in each squad fire team, or designated marksman as they are sometimes referred to, would be issued with the larger 7.62 mm calibre version of the same rifle, the Heckler & Koch HK417 for greater effective range and penetration.

Now the British soldier finally has a weapon that always works and doesn't jam just because a little bit of sand falls in its action or it feels too hot or a bit cold or it's a Tuesday. Not only that, it makes the American soldiers jealous as hell because now we have the best combat rifle in the world, the Rolls Royce of personal weapons.

Oh well, it has only taken thirty years.

My second condition was that my top engineering team be allowed to design a new range of IED-resistant vehicles in partnership with the Army.

IEDs, or improvised explosive devices, are responsible for the vast majority of deaths and life-altering injuries for our soldiers. Therefore, I considered that the development of a vehicle with a very high IED resistance to be one of the highest-priority and most critical military projects of my time in power.

The new vehicles my team came up with have diamond-shaped hulls in profile. They are about same length as the previous vehicles and covered in hundreds of small reactive armour tiles. The hull shape itself deflects blast from every quadrant.

A central control system on the vehicle analyses an IED explosion in milliseconds by reading its heat pattern at the speed of light. It then detonates a quantity of the many small explosive tiles mounted on the exterior of the vehicles back towards the blast path of the IED, not randomly but in a particular order of detonation, creating a pattern that is a unique response to that unique explosion.

The resulting cone-shaped 'wall' of high-velocity armour tiles thus dissipates the IED's energy and so reduces its effectiveness by up to 80 per cent before it even reaches the vehicle's secondary multi-layer armour systems.

The vehicle hulls are dual-skinned, with a 35 mm gap between the twin hull walls, which is filled with a new jelly-like chemical conceptually invented by myself and then operationally developed by my chemistry team. It is called Fragstop.

Should any projectile fragment manage to find its way through the counterblast of the reactive tiles and penetrate the outer skin of multi-layer composite armour, it will by necessity be extremely hot due to friction. As soon as this hot fragment enters this dense, gloopy, jelly-like Fragstop fluid, a limited quantity of the substance instantly solidifies as the result of a chemical reaction triggered by heat.

However, as quickly as this chemical reaction takes place, the heat is also almost as quickly dissipated from the cooling fragment, causing the solidification process to cease just as rapidly. This results in the creation of a solid lump of Fragstop many times the size of the original fragment, which is now trapped in the middle of it.

This process occurs in milliseconds, and takes place just within the first 10 mm or so of penetration of the Fragstop material by the fragment.

This much larger blob of hardened Fragstop now has to force its way through at least another 25 mm of the remaining unaffected soft energy-sapping material. The resistance to this blob, which now has many times the surface area of the original fragment, perhaps as much as one hundred times more, is so great that the fragment's original momentum no longer has sufficient energy to penetrate the inner hull skin and cause casualties.

Special shock-absorbing seats with four-point harnesses from the powerboat racing industry are installed in the interior, setting new standards for crew protection. The counter-explosion of the reactive armour tiles also significantly negates the shockwave damage normally transmitted to the crew, which is often fatal in itself.

The new vehicles are also equipped with a range of highly sophisticated systems for detecting ground-based IEDs such as thermal imagers for detecting buried objects in the path ahead and explosive sniffing devices capable of detecting the presence of explosive chemicals in a highly sensitive and directional manner at up to 100 metres.

Using CCTV cameras from inside, the crew can remotely operate two 7.62 mm multi-barrelled chain-cannon turrets to provide phenomenal firepower without endangering themselves through exposure to the enemy.

These weapons, with a rate of fire of 4,000 bullets a minute each, or 66 per second, are also linked to a short-range radar system capable of autonomously detecting incoming rocket-propelled grenades, known as RPGs, or the deadly wire-guided, Milan-type missiles and disintegrating them in mid-air before they hit the vehicle.

On my insistence no expense was spared on this vital project and, again, section chiefs were ordered to contact me personally to clear any obstacles to the rapid production and deployment of these lifesaving vehicles.

The Army spent their money wisely on a wide range of requirements but I was particularly proud of my team's input into the development of the IED-resistant vehicle.

Amazing what can be achieved with a decent budget and some imagination.

The RAF

Talking about imagination, the RAF still haven't spent any of the money I gave them other than a few quid for some new comfy chairs for their mess halls and some pipe tobacco, because they are still arguing over what sort of planes they want.

I had suggested to them that they draw up a list of all the things they didn't like about the Eurofighter and another list with all the things they would like to have in a new plane and I would make sure it would be built to their specification in double-quick time.

To date, they haven't been able to agree on either list so I have left them to it. I had correctly guessed they wouldn't be able to make a decision about a new plane because aeronautical types can never agree on anything, which is why I didn't give them too much money in the first place.

I am not panicking. The Royal Navy will soon have such a strong Fleet Air Arm aboard its fleet of super-fast scaled-down stealth aircraft carriers, that most of the RAF pilots will be flying Navy planes anyway if the brown stuff ever really hits the fan.

It will be the *Battle of Britain* meets *Top Gun*. 'I say, tally-ho Iceman old bean, what?'

So, long-overdue sensible military budget, GTJD.

Chapter fourteen

Religion

Back in the good old days when the ancient Britons were all pagans and proud of it, a Roman tribune turns up one day and knocks on the door of a Briton chieftain's stockade.

'Ah, good morning, sir. Bit chilly, isn't it? Yes, um, well, I am your local area Roman tribune and, um, it will probably not have escaped your attention that I have a thousand heavily armed troops with me, just over there. With the greatest respect, I see that you on the other hand, have just a hundred or so chaps armed with hunting spears and a few sharpened spades. Now, I suppose that if you were feeling particularly optimistic you might consider having a go at us, but honestly I really wouldn't recommend it. What do you think?'

Chiefy shakes his head.

'Very wise decision, sir, if you don't mind me saying so. I will just write that down. Let's see, oh yes, here it is, the No Immediate Resistance Shown box, just have to tick that. Honestly, all this paperwork they make one do, frightfully tiresome. There we are. Now, regrettably it is my duty to inform you of your options.

'Option one: you retain your status as chieftain of your tribe and carry on as normal except that after every harvest you render a quarter of your crop as tax to the Roman Empire, and um, with regard to this arrangement, we will take your sons to Rome to be educated as Roman gentleman, so that in ten years or so they can come back and take over from you but run the local area the Roman way.

'Option two: you decide that you are not interested in option one and we behead you and your entire family and place your heads on sharpened stakes as an example to the other chieftains in the area. Then we enslave your men and the older women to work on our road-building programme, turn the prettier younger women into comfort girls for the troops, burn your village down and take all your animals and crops.

'Now, which option would you prefer? Look, I'm awfully sorry, old chap, and I really don't mean to put you on the spot, but I would appreciate a decision right away as I do have a lot of other chieftains to visit today. I'm sure you understand.'

Chiefy holds up one finger,

'Oh, that's excellent news. I am so glad. You really have made the best choice for your people I do so assure you, sir. So now if you would just make your mark here at the bottom of the scroll? Wonderful! Thank you so much.

'By the way I'm sure that this is not really necessary to mention, but should you change your mind and organise any resistance against us, we will naturally be posting your sons' heads back in a sack.'

Chiefy shakes his head violently.

'No, of course that won't be necessary. I really am so terribly sorry that I have to mention it. Standard procedure I'm afraid, modus operandi, what? Now you have been so very nice and tremendously cooperative and I really don't want to take up anymore of your valuable time, but I would be so appreciative if you would be so kind as to identify your gods for me so that I can ensure that our men will recognise them and pay them proper respect.

'Perhaps you could ask some of your lovely little chaps to collect them up and lend them to us for an hour? You can? Oh splendid! You really are most awfully kind.'

The wooden idols

The wooden idols, each representing one of the pagan gods are collected up from the various shrines around the village and put on display in front of the assembled Roman troops. Each contubernium, commanded by a centurion, actually consisting of eighty men rather than the hundred most people believe, is then brought forward in rotation to inspect the gods at close quarters.

A duplicarus or sergeant major calls them to attention.

'Shun! Right, lads, stand easy. We are gathered 'ere to *h*inspect these 'ere gods, for what purpose anyone?'

An enlisted man pipes up, 'For the purpose of worshipping them, Sarnt Major?'

'Well done, lad, that's right. They are 'ere for the purpose of worship and don't none of you forget it or I'll 'ave your 'oribble little hides on cobble-polishing duty for the road-building pro-gramme before you can say [his voice rising to a bellow] Julius effing Ceasar.'

'Right, in *h*order to *h*assist you in your duty of worshipping these 'ere gods, I will now *h*identify them for you.'

'God number one for the purpose of worship, is the Briton's god of agriculture. We know him as Saturn, but for reasons best know to themselves, the Britons in their infinite wisdom, call him Farmer Giles. Nevertheless, he is to be granted the same respect due to our god Saturn.

'The second one 'ere is *hey* female god, known as *hey* goddess, in this case the goddess of love and fertility wot we know as Venus. The Briton version 'ere is called Sandra and apparently she comes from Essex, and you will note that her shrine bears a remarkable resemblance to a chariot shelter.'

And so on and so forth, right through the entire pagan god gang.

Why did the Romans go to all this trouble?

Why did the Romans go to all this trouble? Simple, because they were very, very clever and pragmatic people. They knew that you could invade a country, and as long as you had a bigger and better-equipped army, a few isolated pockets of resistance aside, the invaded population would rather let live than resist.

The Romans further appreciated that you could even tax the people you invaded, and again they would lie down and take it.

But screw around with a people's religion, oh no, no, no, that is a very different story.

The Romans had learnt very early in their empire-building that the *one thing* that people will die for is their religious beliefs. You could kill them in the hundreds of thousands but yet they would still never stop coming at you. Worse still, they actually *want* to die as martyrs, which creates a tactical advantage for their side. Ultimately you cannot win without destroying half the country you have invaded and all its valuable resources.

Er, any of that sound familiar at all, hum?

In short, the Romans knew that religion was the one and only thing you didn't mess with. It was just bad for business.

So what have we learnt from the Romans, two and a half thousand years later?

Nothing. That's right; absolutely nothing, bugger all. Nine out of ten wars, seven out of ten violent deaths, ten out of ten suicide-vest bombings, six out of ten rapes, ten out of ten female genital muti-lations, eight out of ten enslavements, seven out of ten paedophile assaults are still all about whose pretendy friend in the sky is the biggest and the best.

Pathetic! Don't talk to me about religion. It is literally the worst thing mankind ever dreamed up. More evil has been done in the name of religion than anything else on the planet.

I simply cannot believe the human race hasn't grown out of it in the twenty-first century.

A priest once asked me whether I believed in Jesus. I said yes, as a historical figure he seemed like a really interesting chap. I would have liked to have had a beer with him.

The priest then asked me why in that case I wasn't a Christian? I replied because I could no more be a Christian than Jesus ever could have been; that's exactly why I admire the man. He despised religion and tried to tell people not to let it mess with their lives.

That's why the Jewish Rabbis with a vested interest in protecting the status quo crucified the poor bloke, and after they crucified him, what happened next? Nothing. That's right – nothing. No fanfares, no trumpets, no new churches thrown up all over the place, no new worldwide religion based on Jesus … nothing.

The disciples understandably got bored and went back to fishing, the Red Sea pedestrians got back to wailing at their wall and chanting at some old rolls of papyrus, and the rest of the world remained happily engaged in worshipping Saturn and Sandra on a Saturday night.

Must have been a rather nice and peaceful period to have lived in, really.

Then, about *three hundred* years later, a group of mates who were all second, third and fourth sons of various wealthy European families, and therefore weren't going to inherit anything from mum and dad due to primogeniture, were sitting around in a tavern one evening having a few bevvies and discussing a script on which to base a new religion and therefore create a massive source of power and wealth.

Today they would have gone into politics, and with their level of ambition, started an illegal war in the Middle East, but the whole politics thing hadn't got going then, as the world was still run by kings and queens, so their options were limited.

Somehow, by good fortune for them, they had stumbled across some old scrolls that they had purchased for a few shekels from a dodgy second-hand camel dealer, picked up on the Jesus story and did a quick spin job on it, like writing up Jesus as a carpenter and Mary Magdalene as a prostitute to appeal to the suppressed masses. Whereas in fact they were both from respectable, wealthy, high-class Jewish families and married to each other, but hey, where was the street cred going to be in that?

Religion and the tabloid press, same brainwashed readership, same deal, never let the truth get in the way of a good story.

With the help of a dodgy but well-connected associate of theirs, Emperor Constantine, who naturally was a lifelong pagan himself (despite pretending to convert on his deathbed for the sake of the business), they then built one of the biggest religions ever created, based very loosely around the now highly modified Jesus story. They named it Christianity.

They gave this new religion a simple cross as a brand, because it would be easy for followers, or franchisees, to recognise and replicate, and then they used the whole circus as a vehicle to create a powerbase for themselves and make a vast fortune out of, while leaving it to mess with millions of people's lives over the next seventeen centuries.

Massacring tens of thousands of innocent people at a time, the Inquisition, torturing, mutilating, raping, burning people alive, branding, looting, enslaving, invading other people's countries, murdering scientists as heretics, repressing women and so on.

Do you really think that's what Jesus would have had in mind? I rather doubt it.

The Crusades

When I said the conspirators who invented the Christian religion would have started an illegal war in the Middle East if they were alive today, I forgot that their efforts actually did lead to exactly that a few centuries later. It was called the Crusades.

Religion aside, purely from the cultural and humanitarian perspective, the Islamic world on the cusp of the twelfth century was the pinnacle of humankind's evolution. Its beautiful cities, each packed with architectural gems and stunning hanging gardens, were open to followers of all religions, including Christians and Jews, who lived happily side by side in peace and prosperity with the easy-going and at that time religiously tolerant Muslim population, because the *real* Islamic faith, as opposed to the version shoved in our faces by the hate fanatics and terrorists today, was based on peace and tolerance.

These cities where great seats of knowledge, intellect and learning, containing universities and libraries full of scientific and cultural knowledge accumulated over the centuries by the highly sophisticated Islamic scholars, including works on astronomy, medicine, chemistry and literature. Scientists today are still discovering things that these learned men already knew some eight hundred years ago.

They could even perform brain surgery back then, for goodness sake, and had invented the analogue equivalent of pocket computers, which could do everything from complex calculations to accurate sun- and star-based navigation, like our pocket-sized GPS systems today.

Mankind looked like it was just about to make it, to actually evolve past violent dispute and grow out of warfare. But right when the human race teetered on the point of finally achieving civilis-ation, into this peaceful utopia tore the Crusades, another religious scam invented in 1095 by a Pope Urban II for purely political and avaricious reasons.

Over the next few hundred years, with the violence of a tsunami hitting a coastal city, successive Crusading armies slaughtered, looted and raped their way through this highly advanced society, burning to the ground some of the most beautiful architecture the world has ever seen, along with libraries full of irreplaceable intellectual treasures, and in doing so, they set mankind back thousands of years and cast us back into the barren wastelands of illiterate superstition, which for centuries the Christian faith relied upon to impose its will on the ignorant masses.

Seriously, to put it in perspective, if it hadn't been for the Crusades we would have colonised other planets by now and cured lethal illnesses like cancer long ago.

The Crusades also created an enemy for all eternity, an enemy we are still fighting a thousand years later and will most probably be still fighting in another thousand.

All this in the name of Christianity, a religion that Jesus had never even heard of, and certainly would never have wanted anything to do with, as to date, it has demonstrably represented everything that he preached hard against all his adult life and ultimately died to stand against.

Just bloody typical, isn't it? It just shows you can't get it right no matter what you do. Poor bloke must have been rolling in his grave ever since.

Anyway, as a dictator I must keep an objective perspective; I must remember that these are just my personal views and I must not let them interfere with running the country.

But I have been worrying about it. I mean what should I be doing about religion in modern twenty-first-century Britain?

Note to self: follow the example of the Romans. Do exactly nothing; just leave it all well alone.

Chapter fifteen

Concorde II and Britannia II

I don't know about you, but every time I saw a *Concorde* take off or come in to land, the hairs on the back of my neck went up and I had butterflies in my stomach. There was something so unbelievably elegant about that plane. With her nose tipped forward, she set down with the gracefulness of a swan.

There is a saying in engineering: if something looks right, it is right. Well *Concorde* was living proof of that. It was simply the most beautiful passenger plane ever built.

When I announced that we were going to build a new supersonic passenger aircraft I was inundated by enthusiastic aeroplane designers eager to show their creations for a more up-to-date, practical and PC-acceptable aircraft. I invited them all to Downing Street for a joint briefing.

I explained that we were not going to build another design of supersonic aircraft; what we were going to build was a spitting image of the original *Concorde*, except very, slightly, imperceptibly larger in size but built to scale so it would not show. It would be brought up to date with modern flight-control systems and more powerful, yet quieter and fuel-efficient engines. When completed the aircraft would be simply be known as *Concorde II*.

They gasped in amazement, but that was because they didn't realise what we were building. We were not just building an aircraft; we were rebuilding Britain's pride.

When they scrapped *Concorde*, using the excuse that a single freak accident caused by debris left on a French runway to wield the final axe, they said it was no longer economically viable. If that were so, how come Richard Branson, the most famous entrepreneur in Britain and not exactly a novice in the air-travel business, wanted to buy the *Concorde* fleet off British Airways? Furthermore, if it was really so unprofitable, why did they not just take the money off the man they regarded as their most serious competitor and run laughing all the way to the bank?

Something never added up about the whole thing, in my opinion, I mean for goodness sake, the fleet had between six and eight years of life left in their airframes and there is no way that a unique service like that could have been unprofitable. Even if it was losing a bit of money, for the sake of our national pride it would have been worth maintaining until a more modern and economical version was built to replace it. Behind the scenes there are always dark forces at work and we must recognise this. Maybe it had something to do with the fact that the Yanks have always resented the fact that we had a supersonic aircraft and they didn't. I have even heard rumours that scrapping *Concorde* was a bargaining chip in a bigger game concerning airport landing slots. Who will ever know?

Whatever the reason, for the first time in mankind's technological evolution we went backwards instead of forwards and that is utterly unforgivable.

Anyway, it doesn't matter now. The new *Concorde II* is up and running and is just as beautiful as the first one, perhaps even more so thanks to a few subtle styling tweaks, and the greatest honour of my life was to present Her Majesty with the first plane, suitably customised in royal blue with the royal crest embossed in real Cornish gold on the tail.

I personally made sure that her interior was suitably customised. My team identified the most comfortable massage chairs available and two of them were installed in a media room, which also contains a massive HD TV screen with surround sound and a digital recorder, set up to record all major horse racing throughout the world twenty-four hours a day.

In another section a comfortable bedroom was installed and

extra seating was provided for the rest of the royal family members if they were coming along. There is also an automatic mechanical running track for the corgis, complete with fully surrounding video screens displaying video and sound and even the smells from the Balmoral or Buckingham Palace lawns so they would feel at home when exercising.

The Royal Concorde was christened *Pride of Britain* and when she made her maiden flight around the entire coast of Britain with the royal family on board, under the escort of six armed Eurofighters, all painted in the matching royal blue livery of the new Royal Protection Flight, all other air traffic was suspended as she made low-level passes over key landmarks and the population looked up, many misty-eyed, and for the first time in years felt the pride swell in them again.

Downing Street was flooded with millions of emails and letters thanking me for relaunching *Concorde*. According to my staff, who read samples of them, many were quite moving and nearly all expressed the sentiment that when they saw her fly by, they felt that they knew for certain that the real Britain was back.

I look forward to their reaction when the new Royal Yacht is launched.

I had the new *Concorde II* built just a tiny bit bigger was so she could have slightly wider seats, and the reason for doing that was a precaution. Just in case there was a thread of truth in the story that the old model wasn't profitable enough, the only reason for this could have been that the seats were too narrow for Americans.

Let's face it, with bankers on both sides of the Atlantic making millions a week and enjoying unlimited expense accounts, you cannot tell me it could have been because the ticket price was too high – no possible way. That simply does not scan, not for the chance to get across the pond in a fraction of the time of a normal plane. Much faster than a private jet, too, let's not forget, and at a fraction of the price.

Time is money in the world of finance. The business hours saved by flying by *Concorde* would always have been far more valuable than the difference in ticket price, which in fact was only slightly more than first class in a normal plane. A banker would spend the difference on champagne and caviar without noticing it.

No, if it there was ever any truth that it did not pay, it could only be that it just wasn't possible for Captain Fast Food to get more than one buttock on a seat. Well, suspecting this to be the case, I made sure the seats are now wide enough even for a 350 lb-burger muncher.

It looks like I guessed right, because every flight is now oversubscribed and we are going to have to build three more to add to the original fleet of four, to meet demand.

Good thing I specified more powerful engines for the new plane, then, or with a full load of oversized Yanks on board we might have had trouble taking off, never mind breaking the speed of sound.

Relaunching *Concorde* and making a commercial success of it. GTJD.

I will leave the last word to Brian Trubshaw, the first British *Concorde* pilot, who said this when he stepped out of the cockpit after her maiden flight on 9 April 1969: 'It was wizard – a cool, calm and collected operation.'

The Royal Yacht

Whoever told us *The Britannia* was an expense this country could not afford should have been hanged at Traitors' Gate. I would have willingly pulled the trap door myself.

The vessel was a floating embassy and the multi-billion-pound deals done on it by British companies paid for its upkeep a thousand times over in export sales. The scrapping of *The Britannia* was an example of politicians exerting their personal power, which as I keep reminding you, is all that elected politicians are about. They take power from the people, not give it to them. They are about stealing away as many of your life values as they can.

By decommissioning *The Britannia* they knew they were stealing a bit of power from the monarchy, reducing its influence and by implication its relevance. The more they do this, the more power they can gain themselves. That is all it was ever about.

You cannot put a price on something like *The Britannia*; it is beyond mere monetary value, you might as well say Buckingham Palace is too expensive and redevelop it into luxury apartments for Russian oligarchs.

The Britannia was our floating embassy, the best in the world, it stood for who we are and what we are, and without it we start to look as bland as the rest of Europe, and that is a terrible fate.

I believe about a year after the original was decommissioned, there was a discussion about building a premier's yacht for the prime minister and senior ruling-party officials. Only of course to help British companies sell their products to the world. Yeah right! Well there's a surprise. *Animal Farm* ring a bell? All non-royal people are equal but some are more equal than others, and the most equal are senior politicians who think they deserve their own yacht.

Anyone who thinks that getting rid of *The Britannia* was justified is missing the point. Even if you are the most ardent anti-royalist you are still missing the point.

If you are the head of some foreign state, it does not matter what your personal politics are; you might even be a raving communist, but you still want to meet a real queen and be invited on her yacht for dinner. You want to feel that you have met the person at the top, above mere politics, a genuine superstar who has travelled the world for decades and knows the political history of every country including your own better than anyone else on the planet because she has actually shaken hands with all the leaders involved over time and invited them on her yacht for a few glasses of top plonk and a really good nosh-up.

It is essential to your own credibility and place in history that you do the same, and no boring jumped-up little prime minister in a cheap suit will do as a substitute. If you are about to award a multi-billion-pound contract to Britain rather than another bidder, you want to feel pampered and appreciated. You want to experience the touch of royalty, bathe in the warmth of its unique glow and feel special.

Only we can do that. No other country in the world can make a head of state feel special but us. Can you imagine the Germans, the French, or even worse, the Italians, trying to make you feel special? Exactly. It doesn't bear thinking about.

No, it is one of Britain's USPs and *The Britannia* played an invaluable role in that, which is why we are now building her replacement without regard to cost.

Naturally, she will be named *Britannia II* by Her Majesty when she launches her on 16 April next year, in memory of the original *Britannia* launched by herself on 16 April 1953.

I have placed her construction under the protection of the Royal Navy in case some ghastly little twerp of a politician tries to sabotage the programme when they return to power. She is being built alongside the new high-tech warships, and the Royal Navy now has the permanent legal authorisation, set in statute, to use lethal force to protect its top-secret dockyards, even from MPs.

Like the new Royal Navy ships, her funding is under the control of three vice admirals and the funds are held in a secret offshore escrow account.

She is about the same size as the original but even more elegant, and, having been constructed out of similar high-tech materials as the warships, is much faster and much more economical. She has her own active camouflage systems and can disappear from sight, radar and thermal detection at the touch of a button.

She is also armed with both active and passive counter-terrorism systems including concealed surface-to-air missiles and the same DEPG death-ray defence system as fitted to our warships, for destroying incoming RPGs or missiles. Again these are completely concealed in such a manner so as not to spoil her elegant appearance.

Her interior has the same blend of luxury and understated class that the original had, only brought more up to date. Any shortcomings on the original have been addressed and she will without doubt be the finest Royal Yacht built to date.

Any ex-crew of the original *Britannia* still of appropriate age have been offered their jobs back when she is ready to sail. Those now too old to serve have had their redundancy and pension packages increased to compensate them for having their jobs taken from them by the duplicitous politicians.

Concorde II and *The Britannia II*, visible proof to the world that Britain *really is back*.

Rule Britannia. GTJD.

Chapter sixteen

Sport

The most important changes to sport have now been implemented as part of the Fat Busting health and fitness programme, which will ensure that every schoolchild gets plenty of exercise playing the normal team sports such a football, hockey, rugby, and cricket.

Other individual sports, including athletics, swimming, tennis, fencing, archery and golf are now receiving substantial additional funding and support from a new programme run by a committee exclusively consisting of ex-athletes and sportsman.

These experienced individuals are employed full time to travel the country and assess the requirements for each local area. Their recommendations are almost always accepted and sports facilities are built in double-quick time. All the normal planning and bureaucratic delays are swept aside. When necessary, I get involved myself.

Hunting

The fox hunting ban was repealed as soon as I took over. The ridiculous ban has resulted in the largest increase in the fox population in the history of Britain, with urban foxes the size of leopards frequently wandering into homes and helping themselves to babies as a quick snack to sustain them on their journey down to the McDonald's food-waste bins.

Due to the impracticality of hunting foxes in urban areas with hounds, I have commissioned a special squad of sharpshooters to roam the streets at night and shoot them with tranquilisers. They are then taken to vets for humane dispatch, as they are too fat and unfit to survive in the wild and if released would only return to urban environments.

At the same time I repealed the ridiculous law limiting stag hunts to two hounds. Now full packs have returned to the field and can once again hunt properly as they have done for hundreds of years.

Pistol shooting

Before the 1997 pistol ban there had never been a single recorded case of a teenager shooting another teenager outside of state-sponsored warfare in the entire four-hundred-year history of fire-arms in Britain. Now in certain inner-city schools, no secondary kid's lunchbox is complete without a 9 mm Glock 17 and they are shooting each other in the playground.

Crime specifically with handguns has risen 400 per cent in the UK since every legally owned one was cut up. Handguns recovered from crime scenes are clearly identifiable by their serial numbers. All of them have being manufactured after 1997 so cannot in any way be linked to the legally owned ones.

This is irrefutable proof that banning legally held guns does not make any impact on firearm crime.

Another factor is that ammunition has never been a problem for owners of illegal guns. Because our firearms laws are drafted by politicians with the square root of zero knowledge about firearms, and then administered by civilian police contractors who know even less, there was a ridiculous loophole in the legislation.

Although guns and manufactured ammunition were licensed, the components of the ammunition were not. Before my time, any drug dealer could walk into a gun shop and buy bullets, cases, primers and powder along with all the tools to put them together for whichever illegal weapons that he may have owned with no licence at all. How crazy was that?

No wonder, then, that when I took over there were more ammunition dumps south of the Thames than the entire Armed Forces had put together. The politicians needn't have concerned themselves about defence cuts; all they had to do was pop down to any pub in Peckham if the Army had run short of bullets.

I put a stop to these ridiculous loopholes and at the same time reintroduced pistol shooting because there was never a genuine reason to ban it in the first place. However, because I do understand firearms, I have done so with a common-sense safety factor built in.

Pistol club members have to leave the barrels of semi-automatics and the cylinders of their revolvers in a safe at the pistol clubhouse.

These vital components, without which the weapons are totally useless and which cannot be purchased separately off licence, are checked in and out by a range officer who takes the car keys and firearm certificate of each member in exchange for his firing parts, which then have to be returned after cleaning before he or she is allowed to leave.

When members shoot at other clubs in competitions, the range officers of the clubs concerned arrange for the secure transportation of the barrels and cylinders.

The cost of this straightforward common-sense safety measure is entirely borne by the club membership, and had this simple procedure been implemented in 1997, it would have prevented the necessity of a ban in the first place and saved the taxpayer millions of pounds in compensation costs.

Had the pistol ban not happened, it is highly likely that there wouldn't be so many illegal weapons on the streets today. Banning things only makes them become more desirable. What part of this simple cornerstone of the human psyche do politicians not understand?

Unbanned the banned sports. Excellent! GTJD.

Chapter seventeen

Fighting Terrorism

Terrorists come in two forms: those who preach it and those who do it. This is how I have dealt with both types.

Terrorists who preach

Anyone who seeks shelter in a host country like ours, lives off our benefit system, is provided with free housing, transport and medical care, and then has the sheer audacity to preach hatred against us and our way of life, deserves no mercy whatsoever.

As soon as I came to power I swept away all human rights previously granted to such loathsome people.

Anyone caught hate-preaching is now instantly deported, along with his wife and children, within a matter of twenty-four hours, either to their country of origin or preferably to any country who wants to interview them in connection with terrorist activities. If that country prefers to do the interviewing without coffee and biscuits, that's all the better as far as I am concerned.

I ordered the SMOG to sweep up all known hate preachers and their families in a single night and every one of them was exactly where they least wanted to be in the entire world before breakfast.

We are watching other suspects carefully now but so far they have kept quiet.

Hardly surprising, really. Do you seriously think that anyone who is wanted in another country and knows that he will be deported there within twenty-four hours to face an unpleasant interrogation or death, is going to preach hatred? Not a chance.

The human rights brigade screamed their heads off, of course, but to their surprise and annoyance none of the population listened to them any more than I did. I ordered the media to give them no more than twenty-four hours of air or ink and so it soon went quiet.

Terrorists who do

The problem with extremist religious nutters is that they want to die as martyrs. This has been a problem for centuries, As I have already said, even the Romans recognised this.

Terrorists rely on terror to achieve their goals. The idea of suicide bombers among us is a terrifying one. Sometimes, however, it is the very thing you fear the most about your enemy that actually conceals their greatest weakness.

Well, the latest lot of pathetic fanatics have got one such serious weakness, and it is as laughably absurd as they are themselves.

They believe that they cannot die while in contact with or covered by the essence of an unclean animal. This is because they believe that if they do, when they enter the next life, the boss of the martyr management department won't grant them the seventy-two virgins they are supposed to be entitled to for blowing up the Number 11 to Piccadilly Circus.

Several animals, such as dogs, are considered as unclean but the one that rates as the most unclean of all animals is the pig. It scores ten out of ten on the unclean list.

Knowing this gave me an idea. I called the new programme, the Pig Squad.

The Pig Squad

Pigs are highly intelligent, sensitive animals that can be trained as easily as dogs and, like their canine counterparts, they have powerful noses and very powerful jaws. I asked my team to find the best pig breeders in the country and offer them a lucrative new career. I realised that the cute little piggy-wiggies were going to save our lives in more ways than one.

Once all the breeders were brought to Downing Street, which upon reflection was a bad move as it took a week for the cleaners to get rid of the whiff, but there we are, I explained to them that I wanted them to take as many suitable pigs as possible to the police and bomb squad dog-training centres and train them to sniff explosives, but with a difference.

When the pigs detected explosive on a person, I wanted them to demonstrate this by jumping up and clamping their extremely powerful jaws onto the private parts of the bomb carriers and hanging on for grim death until they were rewarded with whatever is the ultimate in piggy treats.

Just imagine if you can, the dilemma of the suicide bomber when he finds 500 lb or more of well-motivated Gloucestershire Old Spot clamped on his family jewels. If he detonates his bomb-vest not only will his new best mate in the sky be very reluctant to greet him in the afterlife because he will be covered in pig entrails, and therefore is unlikely grant him his seventy-two virgins, but now he knows that even if an exception is miraculously made, should he press that button, in all probability, as he and Miss Piggy will have separated at approximately 5,000 metres per second, when he arrives there he will no longer have the equipment to do anything to change their status.

In short, checkmate. The only thing he *can do* is surrender.

Even spending the rest of your life in Belmarsh with only your worst enemy for company in the next cell is a better option than any of that.

With some of the above points in mind, I suggested to the trainers that they take suitable precautions to protect the private parts of the training officers during this vital aspect of the training process. They replied that the super-realistic-looking and smelling human dummies the police already used for dog training would do the job fine.

Once the training programme was underway and the first batch of pigs trained, the Pig Squad, in simulated action, was widely publicised on TV and YouTube in order to discourage potential terrorists. It is also repeated on TV every time we get an alert from the intelligence services.

The clamping-onto-the-soft-bits aspect of the training was emphasised in graphic detail with an actor screaming in agony on the soundtrack. This was followed by a hilarious *Family Guy*-type cartoon depiction of a suicide bomber arriving in the next world minus his wedding tackle.

Now, whenever our excellent intelligence services inform me we are on amber or red alert status, every bus in London carries two extra passengers – a smartly turned-out pig and trainer, both wearing uniforms, drawing much admiration and affectionate petting from the animal-loving public, and every tube and train station has at least two of these lifesaving teams in front of the turnstiles ready to welcome any suicide bomber.

During one such recent alert, CCTV footage showed six known terrorist suspects failing to board buses or enter tube stations upon sighting trainers and pigs, both wearing the distinctive high-visibility, bright-pink uniform of the lifesaving Pig Squad.

The action of failing to board buses or enter stations was enough to make the positive ID of the suspects and safely detain them while disarming the devices they were carrying.

Pig Squad, oink, oink. Sometimes it's the simplest things that do the trick. GTJD.

Chapter eighteen

Overseas Aid

Did you know that until I came along we used to send £280 million to India every year and they used to laugh at it and call it a pittance that they didn't need? Well fine, stuff them, because they don't get it now I can tell you. It is all recycled into programmes to deal with the problems of our own poor, along with about 65 per cent of all the other 'foreign aid' programmes that I cancelled.

Consider the irony of this: if instead of giving that £280 million to a country with a GDP of $1,876 billion a year, which can afford to spare $1.5 billion per annum on a space programme, we had looked after our own poor first, we could have used that money to build nearly 3,000 brand-new two-bedroom homes every year for disadvantaged people. By now there would be no such thing as a homeless person on the streets of Britain.

And that is just a tiny fraction of the money we used to give away every year. In total it was over £8 billion per annum.

Many years before I took over the country, I attended a seminar in London at which various third-world countries were asking for their loans to be 'forgiven'. As I sat there listening to the nauseatingly smug representatives of the PCB gobbing off, I looked down the list of countries attending.

Every country on the list but three had corrupt leaders who had squirreled away billions of our generously given aid into secret Swiss bank accounts and other offshore tax havens, purely for their own greedy consumption. Don't ask me how I knew; let's just say it is surprising how closely monitored money laundering is by the intelligence services these days. Terrorism needs cash to operate, ergo … you get it.

Naturally none of the leaders concerned or their representatives were in attendance.

The PCB of course were right there in all their hypocritical glory and riding high on their horses, making it sound like it was the moral duty of the banks to write off the debt. I hate banks as much as anyone, but we all know that asking for the loans to be forgiven is just nonsense. I am sure everyone with a mortgage would like it to be 'forgiven' too because they would rather spend the money on an unnecessary luxury like a yacht or a helicopter.

Well anyway, I was just about to spoil the PCB's day, big time.

I stood up and announced that I was representing the British taxpayer, and as it would in reality be the taxpayer who footed the bill for 'forgiving' these loans rather than the banks, who always pass such costs on in charges or interest-rate increases to their customers, I felt I had a right to point out that I had inspected the lists of countries present and knew that all but three of them had corrupt leaders who had stolen at least 70 per cent of the aid generously donated by the British taxpayer to date.

You could have heard a pin drop. The all-male representatives of fourteen countries silently rose and left, all looking as shifty as if I had caught them trying to pickpocket me. I counted them out as they headed for the gents.

I went on to suggest that before these countries asked us to foot the bill for this corruption, they should first retrieve this stolen money (I paused at this point for dramatic effect and turned to slowly scan the ranks of guilty-looking delegates in the hushed room, none of whom could meet my gaze), then, perhaps if we saw this *stolen money* being returned to the people of their respective countries and used for the good of the general population rather than to provide luxurious palaces and private jets for their leading elite, we might consider 'forgiving' some of the loans.

Another eleven people slipped away, even more hurriedly than the first lot. The gents lavatory must have been getting really crowded.

But here is the thing: although the press was there in all its glory, not one newspaper or TV programme reported what I said. That is an example of how powerful the PCB was before I came along. If you thought Britain had a free press, you were wrong; it had a PCB press. It was free right up to the point that anyone dared to challenge the PCB party line, or the status quo; then it stopped being free real quick and showed itself for exactly what it was. A press completely controlled by the PCB.

As I have already pointed out, we used to give away a £8 billion a year in overseas aid before I came to power. Just imagine how many homes over the years that would have provided for our own poor living well beneath the poverty line.

I am all for helping other countries out, I really am, but my attitude is first let's sort our own country out before giving away taxpayers' money to others.

The 65 per cent of foreign-aid money that I have held back since coming to power has all been funnelled directly into housing homeless people and redeveloping inner-city sink estates – no small change either. To date I have diverted over £26 billion to such projects.

I realise that the politicians may succeed in reversing this when I hand over, but at least many of our own poor will have benefited for once during the five years of my time running the show.

Any overseas aid I do authorise to leave the country now is granted only in genuine emergency situations and carries the condition that it is accompanied by a senior forensic accountant from the FUCU and is guarded by an armed detachment of the SMOG, just to ensure it is being put to the use it was intended for.

In other words, it can only be used to actually buy food and supplies for the starving population, rather than to buy more Lamborghinis for the ruling elite.

If the aid is actually food or physical supplies, my condition is that an armed detachment of the SMOG has to stay with it all the way to its final destination. In many cases, these conditions are accepted. However, it is notable how many so-called 'emergencies' suddenly become downgraded when these conditions are explained.

Funny that, isn't it?

Chapter nineteen

Online Referendum

Now the country is getting back on track, I have to give some thought to what will happen when a democratic government is restored. My fear is that the self-serving politicians will try and undo things, not because there is anything wrong with them but purely to exert their power.

So one measure I have taken to protect the population from the politicians when they return is to make a change in constitutional law. Now, before any law can be changed, it has to meet the approval of a minimum of 75 per cent of the public. This is measured by a new Online Referendum System.

Online referendum based on National Insurance number

A citizen does not even have to be registered to vote, because the systems database has every single person with a National Insurance number on it. In order to vote, all a person over eighteen has to do is log on by entering their National Insurance number and then press the green or red button. Voters abroad on business or holiday can still log on to vote.

If a foreign national who holds a National Insurance number for tax reasons tries to vote, the attempt is rejected because the system can instantly identify that it is not a number registered to a British citizen.

No one can vote twice because the system will only allow one vote per National Insurance number, each one of which it can validate along with the fact that the person is over 18 in a matter of milliseconds before accepting the log in. Simples.

God, I can't help but chuckle when I think how much the politicians are going to hate this new system when they come back into power.

Democracy started off by a spokesman suggesting an idea and then counting a show of hands. The day those individual hands were replaced by so-called elected representatives was the day democracy ceased to exist. It is impossible for any representative to represent the views of the individual who voted for him on every single issue.

But the technology exists today to reverse that. At the press of a button, every adult in the land can now directly have their say on every proposal that will affect their lives.

There has to be a defined timeframe, so the process is swift. Every voter has thirty days to vote on a proposal before the poll closes. By law the BBC must report every current issue currently under vote at the end of every news programme. This is a short broadcast just before the weather forecast to ensure the public is aware of the vote and there is a special website that people can log on to in order to read a full analysis of the subject from both sides of the debate.

Politicians often say that there are issues that are just too complex for the ordinary public to fully understand, and therefore they are not qualified to have an opinion. What a load of patronising bollocks! Look at the average politician today; most of them have never even had a real job in their lives. Who are they of all people to say that they are more qualified than any normal member of the public with a thousand times more real life experience than them?

A simple change in the law and an online voting platform; now that is real democracy. Politicians can sit in parliament dreaming up policies, but now they can only be implemented if the vast majority of the population want them.

Online referendum, really GTJD.

Chapter twenty

Parting Message to the Nation

As the elections draw nearer, the time has come for me to prepare to leave Britain and seek a new challenge elsewhere. So over the last few days I have been writing my farewell message to the nation. What follows is what I will be saying.

Fellow Britons, the time has come for me to leave. By dawn tomorrow you will have a newly elected government. Many of you have been kind enough to ask me to stay and carry on. However, while I am deeply moved and appreciate your support, I have always intended to bring the politicians back to re-establish democratic government, because this is essential for the credibility of our nation in the eyes of the world.

I am confident that all of you will agree that Britain is a much better place today than it was five years ago. Most of you now live a happier, safer, less stressful and more relaxed life than you did before. The economy is booming, there is full employment, crime is all but non-existent, the marvellous new NHS bears no resemblance to its previous form and very few of you pay much, if any, tax at all. Energy costs are down, and our environment is cleaner and less polluted.

When the politicians return, their agenda will be to attempt to change all that. I predict that the first thing they will attempt to do is to replace the Double Up criminal-sentencing system because it is too effective.

Governments pretend to hate criminals but actually they love them because they need them. The last thing they want is a crime-free society. Criminals allow them to create vast bureaucracies, which employ hundreds of thousands of totally unproductive people like criminal psychologists, social workers, parole officers, housing officers and an army of other such people, to look after the criminals.

The larger the bureaucracies become, the more power over the ordinary citizens government and the PCB can establish. You must resist these attempts, no matter how insidiously the politicians and the PCB attempt to dismantle the most effective criminal deterrent in existence. Just ignore their propaganda and vote to retain the existing system.

Equally, I can assure you that unless you are vigilant, they will slowly but surely find a way to tax you again, not because it will be fiscally necessary, as the national debt is now paid off thanks to fracking, and net tax-receipt levels are higher than ever before, but rather it will be because the politicians will want to gain power over you again.

I predict the way they will attempt to achieve this will be to allow the PCB to create a totally false moral argument that the super rich should pay more tax and then raise their taxes. This will result in the rich leaving for a more tax-friendly location, which in turn will result in a massive drain on tax revenues.

This will be the result government will have been seeking, because now they will be able to fabricate a budget which indicates a dire requirement for all citizens to pay tax. It won't be much to start with, just a modest 5 or 10 per cent, but the precedent will have been set. Once the conventional tax system is re-established, they will never stop raising taxes until they have you back where you started, at their mercy.

Do not allow them to get away with it. Fight them to your last breath for your freedom, or once again you will become no more than the taxed slaves of the government, like our ancestors used to be to the Romans and the Normans.

I am just as certain that the PCB will call for an end to corporal punishment and compulsory sport in schools. They will claim human rights are being abused. The government will listen sympathetically to their pleas, not because they are so stupid that they fail to realise that these measures have proved themselves highly effective over the last five years. No, rather it will be because it suits their agenda to return to the old ways.

Not only does it suit government to have plenty of criminals, it also needs overweight and unfit schoolchildren, which is exactly why they allowed the schools to sell off all the playing fields in the first place. Fat children grow up into obese citizens in adulthood and develop illnesses such as heart disease and diabetes, and so become more dependent on government for services such as health care, the purse strings of which the politicians hold.

The more dependent and unhealthy the population becomes, the more power the politicians have over them. Government is a parasite, and all parasites have to feed off the life force of their host to thrive. It will find itself struggling to survive in a crime-free and healthy society and so it will conspire to change that status quo.

It is not only big government you have to keep a watchful eye on. You must be wary of other establishment groups such as the police. They will soon tire of actually policing the roads properly and want to slip back into their old ways of doing the least possible work for the greatest amount of revenue. If you allow them an inch they will take a mile.

Report illegal speed traps right away and ensure that you obtain a written acknowledgement of your complaint from the police force in question, and then send this to your MP and demand that he deals with it.

Open-road average speeds, outside of urban areas, have never been higher in the history of this country, yet the accident rate has never been lower. Remember these salient facts. Do not allow the police to resume their dishonest anti-speed propaganda purely for their own benefit.

Remember above all else that politicians are not your allies; they are your enemies, whose main agenda is to take as much as they possibly can from you while fooling you into thinking that they are acting in your best interests.

The various political parties are merely part of their camouflage and there is no fundamental difference between them, left, right or centre. Sadly we have to put up with them as a necessary evil, like traffic wardens, but never for one second put your trust in them or let your guard down.

Watch for their every attempt to steal away your life values for their own empowerment.

The last five years will go down as an anomaly in this island's history, and I do not resent that. Some of the ruthless measures I took will result in me being labelled unflatteringly in decades to come. I simply don't care. I was never in this business for glory. I took such drastic measures as were necessary to save the country from disaster and that is the end of it.

I have no doubt that the people who will criticise my actions the most vocally will be the duplicitous PCB who were originally responsible for causing most of the problems that I have solved. Once I am gone, they will crawl back out of the woodwork, and by applying pressure to the gutless politicians, start to re-establish their evil powerbase again.

Only you, the ordinary people of Britain can stop them. Do not rely on the politicians to help you, they will be too busy finding ways that the PCB can assist them in repressing you.

I wonder, however, how historians in the future will reconcile the ironic fact that it has taken a dictator to give you your freedom and the chance to retain some influence over your own destiny through the introduction of the most significant return to real democracy in history, the Online Referendum System.

There are many things that my small team and I have achieved over the last five years, which as a patriot give me great pride: the strongest economy in Europe, total energy self-sufficiency, a new National Health Service that is now the envy of the world, full employment, a much healthier, fitter population, a well-funded and highly effective Armed Forces, the new Royal Yacht *Britannia II* and of course the new unique and highly profitable *Concorde II* super-sonic transatlantic service.

To see our prestige in the world rise to where it once stood is all the reward I sought. Just to watch so many of you around the country on TV cheering at the launch of the new *Britannia II* and at the sight of *The Royal Concorde* flying over your towns, to feel the swell and resonance of your pride, to sense the electricity in your collective emotion, was all it took for me.

Really, when I come to think about it, just to see the look of pride on the face of one of our vice admirals when he inspected the first new stealth destroyer under construction was worth the whole exercise in itself.

But of all those achievements a single one tops them all – the legal integration of the Online Referendum System into our constitution, a revolutionary use of contemporary technology to return mankind to the very birth point of democracy itself.

With this parting gift, I have left you, the people of Britain, with the mechanism to protect yourselves from the tyranny of politicians, the greed of bankers and from the evil, underhand agendas of the PCB.

So please, I implore you to use the Online Referendum System to fight all of these self-interested groups for your freedom and your way of life. Fight them every single day and never compromise or give in.

For the first time in our island's long and distinguished history, you are a truly free people now. It is the duty of each and every one of you to ensure that it stays that way, and that for evermore the politicians will remain your servants and never again rise to become your masters.

When I board my plane to leave Britain's shores for the last time tonight, though I will be doing so with a heavy heart because I can never return, I will at least go knowing that I am leaving the country I love as the only genuine democracy in the world.

Good bye and good luck to you all. Yes, I certainly Got The Job Done, GTJD!